HEALTH ADMINISTRATION IN A METROPOLIS

HEALTH ADMINISTRATION IN A METROPOLIS

Usha Banerjee, M.A., Ph.D.

ABHINAV
PUBLICATIONS

Abhinav Publications, New Delhi . 1976

The Indian Council of Social Science Research gave
financial support towards the publication of this work.
However, the responsibility for the contents of the book—
facts, opinions, conclusions etc.—is entirely that of the
author and not of the ICSSR.

© Usha Banerjee

First Edition : 1976

Publisher : Shakti Malik
          Abhinav Publications
          E 37 Hauz Khas
          New Delhi-110016

Printer   : Dhawan Printing Works
          26-A, Mayapuri Phase I
          New Delhi-110027

Dedicated to my beloved mother
who inspired me
to work and write this book

Foreword

I am happy to write this foreword to the study of health administration in a metropolitan community by Dr. (Mrs.) Usha Banerjee. The study describes the organisational framework of health services within the Delhi Municipal Corporation and against this background undertakes an analysis of the many problems of health administration. Among the problems she discusses are those that arise from a particular mode of job distribution and from the practice of entrusting decision-making to committees of elected representatives who are constrained by political considerations. She also discusses the familiar problem of ensuring unity of control in a situation where specialist, professional functionaries are professionally supervised by their parent department and are yet dependent upon and accountable to a ward or district-level bureaucrat. The problems are not new but their discussion gains in depth and vividness since it relates to specific situations.

The data for Dr. Banerjee's study are derived from municipal records and from a direct opinion-survey in a small municipal area. Her data show that municipal health services are unequally distributed as between different areas of the city. The localities which are inhabited by the poorer segments of the population are also the ones with high population densities. Their need for public health services is particularly great and yet under our present pattern of distribution it is not uncommon for these needy areas to receive less of the services that a municipality can offer. This situation has broader implications from the point of view of the egalitarian social goals that we profess.

In the various campaigns for control of communicable diseases, the Delhi Municipal Corporation seems to have made considerable headway, but its family planning services are far too inadequate. The staff is inadequate in number and, in Dr. Banerjee's view, it is also inadequately trained and not sufficiently motivated. Her analysis also brings out the fact that family planning services are not well-integrated with the total health services.

It is difficult to undertake an overall assessment of any programmes of social service such as health or education. Most often, such assessment is in terms of achievement or non-achievement of specific physical targets. Dr. Banerjee naturally falls back on these measures and highlights the shortfalls in achievement. But, additionally, she also comments on certain shortcomings which may account for less-than-adequate performance. She underlines the difficulties of implementing health legislation relating to communicable diseases or adulteration of food articles, etc. She characterises certain of the procedures followed by the department as time-consuming and complicated. She points to the absence of supportive social services which make health services ineffective.

Toward the end Dr. Banerjee discusses the personnel administration needs of the department and undertakes an appraisal of its personnel policies.

The social science literature on health administration is not extensive. Studies of the type that Dr. Banerjee reports upon in this volume are, therefore, welcome both for the factual information they present and the analytical framework in terms of which they are sought to be discussed.

Bombay-400088   M.S. GORE
May 16, 1975   *Director*
                                              Tata Institute of Social Sciences

Acknowledgements

I am grateful to Prof. S.N. Ranade and Prof. V. Jaganna-dham for their guidance in this study. I am indeed thankful to Dr. M.S. Gore for writing foreword to my book.

I am thankful to the Director and staff of National Institute of Health Administration and officials of the Health Department, Delhi Municipal Corporation for their cooperation in this project.

I am indebted to the Director and staff of Indian Institute of Public Administration and Delhi School of Social Work for all the help they extended to undertake this work.

I am grateful to Shri J.P. Naik of Indian Council of Social Science Research for taking special interest in my project. I sincerely appreciate Dr. Chaturvedi's help in reviewing the manuscript.

Lastly, I am grateful to my husband Dr. (Col.) R.N. Banerjee, Senior Physician of Safdarjang Hospital for his professional guidance and constant encouragement in my work.

New Delhi   USHA BANERJEE

List of Map and Figures

Contents

HEALTH ADMINISTRATION IN A METROPOLIS

CHAPTER I

Introduction

Growing urbanization poses a newer set of challenges to the civic administration : it is confronted with varied and complex problems. Changes in the values and in the social structure, consequent upon the mobility of population, necessitate continuous thinking on the part of the urban administration.

A growing metropolis represents all the processes connected with urbanization. Several aspects of urban life conglomerate and hinge upon the core and periphery of metropolitan area. Delhi is one of the largest metropolises in India, as far as her urbanization pattern and population composition is concerned.[1]

The responsibility of urban government, in building up civic administration capable of providing basic amenities to local population is immense. Among others, health and education are regarded vital components of civic life. Most of the services provided by the metropolis are essentially of social service nature, which stipulate a special "users" rather than "private gain" orientation. Furthermore, there has to be integration and coordination of all welfare activities to cater to the wide variety of needs of the community.

---

1. According to 1971 Census, 89.75% of total population of Delhi is living in urban area.

In a relatively slow moving economy, as in India there are enormous difficulties in effective implementation of metropolitan services by the local government. On the one hand, there has been a rapid socio-political development with an increasing demand on attainment of results. On the other hand, a complex administrative system to keep pace with the special expectations has led to a widening gap between the assumption of role and the responsibilities of the local administration. This is evidenced more in case of administration of social services, which is directly concerned with welfare of the community.

The study of administration as a separate discipline is of recent origin in India. The subject of local administration and particularly social services has not so far received adequate attention. There are, however, several studies on urban local government dealing with the formal structural and financial aspects but very little systematic effort has been made to analyse socio-administrative processes. Except two surveys conducted by the Indian Institute of Public Administration,[1] no other systematic study report is available on the subject. The present study is, therefore, an effort in the direction; it is, however, confined to the Health Department of the Delhi Municipal Corporation.

The study attempts to :

(i)   analyse the organisational structure of the Department in its historical context;

(ii) describe and analyse the performance of the Department with special reference to its existing organisation, personnel policy, finances, and public relations;

(iii) identify the problem areas in administering services and indicate their interrelationship; and

(iv) develop alternative guidelines for administrative system relevant for social welfare services.

1. Indian Institute of Public Administration Studies :—
   (a) V. Jagannadham and N.S. Bakshi : *Citizen and Municipal Bureaucracy* (A survey of the Building Department of the Delhi Municipal Corporation, I.I.P.A., New Delhi, 1971).
   (b) V. Jagannadham and N.S. Bakshi : *Property Tax Administration* (A study of the collection and assessment department of the Delhi Municipal Corporation, I.I.P.A., New Delhi, 1971).

Delhi, as a Capital City, has many administrative agencies such as Central Government, Delhi Administration and a multitude of voluntary organisations besides the Delhi Municipal Corporation, to provide services in health and family planning, for the citizens in Delhi. In order to have a focussed study, the present exploration is confined to the administration of the Health Department of the Delhi Municipal Corporation only. The outlines of the objectives mentioned above would indicate that this micro-study is restricted only to the areas of personal and public health (preventive, curative and family planning services) administration in relation to their organisational structure, functions, legal framework, procedure, management of personnel, finance and public relations as adopted by the Health Department of the Corporation. This study does not envisage to cover people's expectations of the benefits from the Health Department, and their evaluations of its performance; nor does it attempt any cost-benefit analysis in economic terms.

Review of the Available Literature and Need for the Study

The available studies on the subject could be classified in two groups, viz., (a) local administration of health and welfare services in general in a few Western countries; and (b) health and family planning administration in India.

Studies in the Western Countries

In a comprehensive ecological survey of welfare services in Greater London based on documentation study, Ruck (1963) highlighted the diversity of quality and quantity of the welfare services in that city. It further revealed communication barrier and lack of coordination among various departments resulting from piecemeal legislation and decentralisation. The study, therefore, suggested administrative reorganisation. Julia Parker (1965) is more specific about the administration of the health and welfare department of the local body to prove her case for uncoordinated social administration in London. She reported that absence of coordination emanates from absence of any clear-cut definition and analysis of the role and responsibilities of different organisations. The modern complex government involving the highest degree of specialisation makes the coordination more difficult. She questions whether local authorities are effective instruments to provide meaningful services of health and welfare to the people. She points out that the concept of universalism and egalitarian principle is limited in two ways :

(1) lack of money, resources, equipment, accommodation and personnel; and
(2) geographical pattern of welfare services, varying from area to area.

She points out that the idea of community care as developed in recent years has enhanced the financial responsibilities and the area of coordination of local administration. Unless the normative frame is properly worked out in detail and accepted the field level staff would only cooperate to the extent they find it advantageous. The shortage of dedicated qualified staff for welfare and health department and the need to appoint qualified social workers in all these departments is exphasised in her study.

Robson (1954), Hauser and Philip (1959) in their studies on urbanisation also mentioned similar administrative problems. In a recent sociological study on urban problems in the U.S.A., Sharrard (1968) edited a collection of papers on the role of social welfare as a prerequisite for the achievement of a more humane society.

In a book on Manpower Strategy (Ginzberg 1968), containing a series of articles on manpower problem of New York City, Carol Brown (1968) discusses the expansion of health services in the New York City and clearly brings out the growth of medical and health care as one of the major industries there.

The report of the Commission on the delivery of personal health services (Praguer 1969) in Community Health Services in New York City is based on direct interviewing of the staff of the municipal hospitals of the the city of New York. The report provides valuable policy guides for future health planning of a city.

Anderson and Anderson (1967) in their recent book on *A Decade of Health Services* made an analysis of how people in the United States use health service system. It is based on a study of representative samples of the families drawn at five-year intervals from 1953 through 1963. It shows the viewpoint of the beneficiaries of personal care services. However, administrative management aspect is not included in its purview.

The role of area planning, the problem of integration of regional hospitals with other services, specially the local authority services, have been the subjects of discussion in some of the operational research studies (Forsyth 1962 : 70). Could a change in the regional structure of these services yield a better integration ? And with what consequences for area planning ? Is the present management of the health services consistent with its aims and functions ? Hospital services are arranged geographically and local health authority services are keyed to the local government structure. Does this difference in administration affect integration at local level ? The report on Cooperative Research in Health Services reviews its basic design and functions, effectiveness and efficiency of the services. While measuring the quality of services, the author raises many questions, e.g., measurability of effectiveness and qualitative evaluation of routine system of supervision.

It is rather difficult to evaluate the health services in the absence of any well defined conceptual framework. There are great variations in the normative standards in hospital services in different countries. Sometimes an index of efficiency is the average duration of stay in a specialist department of a hospital. But this average duration of stay in hospital is an inadequate measure, as it does not take into account the re-admission ratio. Secondly, it is difficult to know about the whole course of treatment from the onset of illness to the return to work. In a public service with variation in demands and needs, the definition of "efficiency cost" is bound to be a source of debate.

Thus, the question arises whether the available resources are really reliable in studying the medical care in the society.

Studies in India

Available information on the study of health administration in this country is meagre. It is only very recently that attempts have been made to carry out some studies.[1] In the Third Report of the W.H.O. Expert Committee on Public Health Administration, the local health services in India, along with Netherlands, Puerto Rico, Sweden and Africa, have been reviewed.[2] The variables studied were : (i) general background, (ii) present health services available, (iii) health personnel, (iv) financing and cost of health services, (v) development of health services since 1900s, (vi) general description of social and economic changes since 1900s, (vii) statistical and other data; and (viii) adequacy of health services.

The results of an extensive study carried out in Delhi, Kerala, Madras, Maharashtra, Punjab and U.P. States by collaborating teams of John Hopkins Rural Health Research Project have been published (Takulia 1969). The study attempts to determine the opinions of the selected groups responsible for directing the actual work of the health centre activities and also identifying problems in the present administrative set up. Besides, it suggests alternatives for administrative reorganisation. The findings, however, indicate that most of the respondents regard health centres as multi-service units for the promotion of community welfare, but the response to the specific objectives of the Primary Health Centre varied. The State legislators and the Medical College teachers showed lack of familiarity with the health centre activities other than the curative services. The survey suggests that the doctors have a heavy clinical workload and have less interest and time for preventive work. About 77 per cent reported

1. A number of administrative questions were also posed in *Fifth Report of the Expert Committee on Public Administration of Urban Health Services* (T.R. 250, 1963).

2. The study of local health services in India was done in respect of Ramnagram Health Training Area, Mysore, India. The study revealed that the combination of preventive and curative services has paved the way to the health education. *Third Report of the Expert Committee on Public Administration of Urban Health Services* (Notes from W.H.O. Technical Series No. 194, 1960).

that the friction between the Doctor and Block Development Officer was due to dual control over the staff and for the "Doctor's prestige" in the community. The doctor demanded the administrative independence whereas the administrators thought that both the officers should be made responsible to the Block Samiti.

This monograph is informative on the problem of health administration at the primary health centre level. As a piece of research work, it tends to be an opinion survey of a limited nature. Many of the conclusions are of common knowledge to those, who are searching for effective methods in the field of health administration. Moreover, it is partial in the sense that it deals only with the health services in rural areas and the beneficiaries were not included in the study.

The foregoing review clearly suggests that we have very little systematic information on administrative aspects of health and family planning at local level. However, the large mass of information available is based on the Western experience, which might fail to provide fruitful guidelines, in the local context. Hence there is need to have systematic studies dealing with the administrative and organisational aspects of urban local government and the present venture is an attempt in that direction.

The Planning Commission of the Government of India has used the term 'Social Service' to cover a broad range of welfare measures and programmes including education, health, family planning, housing, urban and rural development, welfare of backward classes, scheduled castes and tribes and social welfare. But it has given a rather narrow connotation to the term social welfare service and social administration. We shall, however, be using this definition so that our evaluation of the services can be put in a proper context.

Social Administration vis-a-vis Public Welfare Administration

According to R. Clyde White (1950 : 4), public welfare administration is considered as an art and science of those governmental activities which are directed towards the relief of distress, the care of dependent and neglected children, the treatment of criminals and delinquents and the care and treatment of mentally ill. It is public welfare organisation in operation. Therefore, public welfare administration is social administration minus the services rendered by the voluntary organisations for the welfare of the people, that is, of the community. Thus it appears that the term public welfare administration has a narrower coverage than social administration.

Social Administration and Social Policy

Social policy seeks to bring change through social action in a problematic situation. Titmuss (1968) has clearly indicated that social administration is centred round the social institutions which unites the objective (end) of social policy and the development and administration of public and voluntary organisation (means). Marsh (1964 : 15) and Lafitte (1962) however suggest that social administration is an instrument of bringing social action through implementation of social policy. It is a dynamic concept, varying from State to State on its stages of development.

Marsh constantly reminds us of the need to study 'social policy' in the socio-economic perspective of the country, which is constantly changing. Social administration here is a process of bringing community welfare through social change in its process of implementing social research and social policy decisions for the total welfare of the community. Jagannadham (1964 : 132-135) also accepts this view when he says, social administration is concerned with providing "services" to the citizen. To him, social administration is administration of "social services" and it is distinguished by an "over-riding concern for the welfare of human being."

The motivation of social administration is the basic human desire to help each other. The humanitarian idealism based on the redistributive egalitarian principle pervading the field of social welfare and social work brings it close to social administration. It is also based on the concept of universality of services.

Health Administration

World Health Organisation, in its constitution, proposes

that health be considered "...a complete physical, mental and social well being, and not merely the absence of disease or infirmity." Winslow, in defining health, includes "preventing disease, prolonging life, promoting physical health and efficiency." (1951 : 28) Thus the elements of preventive, curative and rehabilitative and promotive aspect of social welfare are involved in the complex gamut of health administration. Accordingly, the private practitioner and governmental agencies all contribute to health administration. The health administration thus has a very complex, broad and comprehensive scope which forms a major responsibility of any metropolitan government.

Enfry states, "The administration of the community health services in a local health department is the application of administrative techniques, public health practice and social science in an organised community." (1964 : 10) In other words, it is an aggregate of the administrative processes and methods which are used in carrying out health department's objective through organised community effort. Health is a social responsibility in and out of the community. Municipal or local health problem according to modern health administration is community problem.[1] As used in this study the term community refers to entire population of a functionally defin-

1. Concept of community health is of recent origin. In studies of Stamper & Grant and later by Leavell, it has assumed great importance. The aim of medical science, whether applied to individual or community, is to help achieve such a well being that one may function at the optimum not as an individual but also as a useful member of the family, social groups and the community. The concept is the 'total health' for 'total man'. The services designed to provide health care under this concept must include promotive, preventive, curative, restorative, and rehabilitative aspects organised and integrated in a unified manner. Community health problem is manifested through an acute epidemic, communicable and non-communicable diseases, widespread malnutrition, population explosion, problem of expectant and nursing mothers, infants, preschool and school children and industrial worker. There may be also prolems by accidents, stream pollution, safe water supply, sewage disposal, disposal of human or animal waste. The aim is to meet "health need" within available resources of the community. It is through community approach, people's cooperation in the programme can be ensured.

ed geographic area that has developed common interests, activities and interrelations.

The health care needs in an area, on the other hand, are dependent upon (a) population profile; (b) urbanization and industrialization creating further demand for health services; (c) utilising knowledge concerning factors that influence health care; (d) available tools and their efficiency in dealing with specific health problems; (e) health care priorities in relation to limitation of resources like trained personnel and financial resources; and (f) adequate structure and organisational system and their responsiveness to the needs of the people.

In the administration of health department, therefore, as Freeman and Holmes (1964 : 50) put it, the following steps are involved :

(a) Planning including community diagnosis, forecasting, setting objectives, budgeting and phasing.

(b) Mobilising, including motivation of staff and community staffing, functional team organisation, organisational structure and delegating.

(c) Coordinating all different elements and groups engaged in health problem for preventing duplication.

(d) Guiding including reconciliation of programme, preventing duplication, establishing communication.

(e) Guiding the control of quality and quantity, evaluating outcome, establishing policies and procedures.

(f) Liberating including discovering worker, people, developing people, providing diversified experience and opportunity, developing community leadership.

(g) Accounting, including reporting to people or representatives of public about fiscal management.

Components in Urban Health Administration

The health administration in an urban metropolis because of its complexity of problem calls for the best managerial practice. The responsibility of community health is shared by the following :

(a) The individual.

(b) Private practitioners.
(c) Official health agencies, local health department and Central and State hospitals and clinics.
(d) Other official agencies related to health problem.
(e) Voluntary health agencies and welfare organisations.

It is the task of the chief executive of the municipal health administration to coordinate the work of all these agencies. The objective is to provide a "healthful community".[1] The term "healthful community" is related to the stage of development of one community and the attitude and value of the community to that problem. In India, the "healthful community" is defined in minimal terms; such as adequate preservation of sanitation and cleanliness, prevention and control of infectious and water-food-milk borne diseases and medical relief to the deserving cases. The present study is confined to the health and family planning services, provided by the Health Department of the Delhi Municipal Corporation.

Methodology

The research method used for the present study is survey-cum-evaluation of a unit of social administration. It comprises the survey of the current practices, procedures, problems of management, formulation of certain criteria and evaluation of the current practices in terms of these criteria. The information is drawn from primary and secondary sources. While the secondary sources consist of published and unpublished reports, documents, files, acts and bye-laws; primary sources include field study of the South Delhi Zone[2] and some other institutions in different parts of the metropolis as well as informal interviews with the members of the health services staff

1. In Western countries, in most of the cities and countries, administrators interpret a healthful community in positive terms as well, that is, a place where suitable recreational facilities are provided, where planned urban and suburban development is conducive to mental hygiene, where living and working are comfort and not merely convenience.
2. Delhi Corporation area is divided into eight zones for decentralisation of administration, as discussed in Chapter II. Details about South Zone are given in the subsequent pages.

in Town Hall and South Delhi. Besides, a limited number of beneficiaries were also interviewed in the outdoor department. South Delhi Zone was selected for the purpose.

Informal discussions were held with senior officials of the Health Department, Ford Foundation Consultants on Health Administration, members of the staff of the National Institute of Health Administration and Education, the teaching staff of Delhi School of Social Work and with prominent citizens in the field. About ten dispensaries and three hospitals managed by the Corporation were also visited.[1] 25 beneficiaries of the hospital outpatient department, as well as ten staff members such as dealing clerks and sweepers, were informally interviewed. These preliminary discussions provided good deal of information and insight which formed the basis of the present research design. In addition, the Fifth Staff Training Course on Health Administration arranged by the National Institute of Health Administration and Education was also attended to collect information on technical aspects of Health Administration.

During the initial stages, various important suggestions on methodolgy were received. Some of these suggestions could not be pursued as they did not fall within the purview of the study and were not practicable. One of the suggestions was to interview some of the old and new beneficiaries of the municipal health services. It was pointed out that the study would remain incomplete unless the public attitude and feeling towards health services were not properly looked into. It would have been better to study the users of the services. But this could not be pursued owing to various considerations. Problems were faced while selecting the hospital patients and the clients at the outdoor department of the dispensaries. Another suggestion was to interview patients of the Lajpat Nagar Hospital, who were admitted during the period of 1965-66 on a random sample basis, taking that as the mean year for 1959-1969 period. Again there were several operational problems and hence the idea was abandoned. Another important suggestion was that, the researcher should work in some of the sections of the

1. See the list of institutions managed by the Corporation, shown in Appendix A.3.

Health Department for some time and also visit the rural areas administered by the Corporation. As far as possible this suggestion was conceded to. A group of beneficiaries were interviewed during one month when the researcher regularly visited the outdoor department of the dispensaries and other hospitals of the Corporation. The information from the interviews proved to be useful.

Secondary Source : Documentation

First phase of the study involved scrutiny of the official documents which included Acts, Bye-laws, administrative reports, administrative directives, memos on procedure, official memoranda, training manuals, financial and establishment reports, handouts and health intelligence reports of the vital statistics section, agenda and proceedings of the Standing Committee and of the Medical and Public Health Committee meetings, audit reports and various relevant files of the last ten years.

Administrative directives are of three types, viz., (a) Delhi Administration Health Department to the Corporation; (b) Union Health Ministry to the Health Department; and (c) Commissioner or Health Officer to his subordinates. An attempt was made to study all available documents related to the Department.

Primary Source : Survey of Current Practices

In order to gain information on current practices and the administrative problems, one zone was selected. Initially it was planned to study two or three zones in depth but later it was decided to cover one representative zone embodying all the heterogeneous characteristics of the urban metropolis. Hence the case study method was applied in regard to South Delhi Zone. South Delhi Zone represents geographically all the characteristics of Delhi. Besides it encompasses several services of the Health Department. This zone, which has seen a rapid urbanisation,[1] is characterised by a set of con-

1. The population in South Delhi Zone has increased from 55,815 to 1,15,577 during 1951 to 1961 period.

gested low income group colonies, such as, Kalkaji, Kotla
Mubarakpur, Bhogal, Sewa Nagar, Ashram, Madangir and
Nanak Pura, Vinay Nagar, Arjun Nagar in contrast to Friends
Colony, Defence Colony, Hauz Khas, Maharani Bagh, Green
Park, South Extension and Panchsheel Marg[1] etc. The area is
also served by big hospitals like Holy Family, Safdarjang and
All India Institute of Medical Sciences and a number of
Central Government health service dispensaries. Two rural
health centres, e.g., Mehrauli and Fatehpur Beri are also
located in this zone. By selecting South Delhi Zone it was
intended to highlight the administrative practices and problems
in an area of low density and high literacy. In the final stage,
however, visits to the dispensaries in Town Hall and S.P.
Mukherjee Marg, T.B. Clinic and Sadar area M.C.H. Centre
for observation of institutions provided sufficient material
for generalisation. The number of the institutions in this
selected area being small, an attempt was made to visit all the
institutions under the South Delhi Zone.

Selected Zone

The South Delhi Zone, as we find, is surrounded by the
New Delhi Municipal Committee in the north, by West Zone
of Delhi Municipal Corporation and Haryana State in south,
and the river Yamuna in the east. According to 1961 Census,
area of South Zone was 24.76 square miles, covering 4.32 per
cent of the total area of Delhi. Since last 1961 Census, certain
portion of the transferred area of the Corporation has been
allocated to South Zone, expanding the area. The density of
population here is 1,802 per square kilometre against average
density of 1,791 per square kilometre in Delhi. About 48.2
per cent of the total population is literate, against 52.8 per cent
average literacy in Delhi, as per 1961 Census figures. Bhogal,
Nizamuddin, Okhla, Mehrauli and Badarpur areas have a
sizeable Muslim population. Okhla and Badarpur areas constitute the industrial belt of Delhi. South Zone is comprised
of twelve municipal constituencies and sends fourteen muni-

---

1. These are some private residential colonies inhabited by upper
income group.

cipal councillors to the Corporation. The area evidenced great urbanisation during the last ten years and expanded through a number of newly emerged private and government colonies.[1]

The Health Department here performs all the different categories of health activities of the Corporation on a minia- ture scale. It provides services, *viz.*, environmental sanitation, licensing of foodstuffs and sampling, removal of unhygienic foodstuffs according to Food Adulteration Act, sampling of water disinfection, school health programme, ambulance service, hospital and dispensary, veterinary hospital, notifica- tion of cases of infectious diseases and vaccination, destruction of rats, funeral service, and family planning service. Zonal Health Office at Green Park is controlled by Assistant Zonal Commissioner. The Zonal Health Officer assisted by the Chief Sanitary Inspector with a small secretariat manages the health problems of the zone. Table I.1 shows that the immunization and other public health services are provided through Sanitarians, Vaccinators and Sweepers, whereas the medical contingent consists of Doctors, Nurses, Paramedicals and Class IV employees. Three Colony Hospitals (100 beds), Urban Health Centres, Veterinary Hospital, Rural Health Centre (16 beds), Maternity and Child Health Centres and Sub-Centres are located here.

Data Collection through Interview Schedules

Separate sets of interview schedules were framed for each category of personnel as a guide for discussion. Besides, a general interview schedule was also used for all these categories of staff. These are given in Appendix C.

Schedule type A was used for officers at the Head Office, the Deputy Commissioner (Health), Accounts Officer, Deputy Health Officer, Statistical Officer, Malaria Officer, Administrative Officer, Zonal Health Officer and Assistant Zonal Commissioner.

Schedule type B was used for the health executives, doctors in the hospitals and dispensaries, Sanitary Inspectors in charge of Public Health Centres.

1. Government record indicates that there were 324 new housing colonies in Delhi during the period 1965-66.

TABLE I.1

Institutions and staff of different categories in South Delhi Zone

Institutions & Areas	Doctor	Sanitarian	Dispenser	Dresser	Nurse	Midwife	Lady Health Visitor	Vaccinator	Class-IV Staff
1. Head Office Green Park	1	2	—	—	—	—	—	—	—
2. Colony Hospital :									
a–Malviya Nagar	3	3	3	1	3	1	1	1	17
b–Kalkaji	3	—	3	1	3	1	1	1	17
c–Lajpat Nagar	7	—	4	1	6	1	1	2	21
3. Urban Centre, Defence Colony	1	—	1	1	—	—	—	—	—
4. PH Centre :									
a–Mehrauli	2	—	—	—	2	1	1	—	5
b–Fatehpur Beri	2	—	—	—	2	1	1	—	5
5. Dispensary :									
a–Jangpura	1	—	2	1	—	—	—	—	—
b–Madangir	1	—	1	1	—	—	—	—	—
c–Badarpur	1	—	1	—	—	—	—	—	—
d–Madangir Camp	1	—	2	1	—	—	—	—	—
6. Vet. Dispensary :									
a–Ghetoni	1	—	1	1	—	—	—	—	—
b–Mehrauli	1	—	1	1	—	—	—	—	—
7. F.W. Centre—19	9	—	—	—	—	14	14	—	—

N.B. There are also 9 Pay Clerks, 14 Sanitary Inspectors, 44 Assistant Sanitary Inspectors, 14 Sanitary Guides, 56 Beldars, 13 Drainage Sweepers, 1,313 Permanent Sweepers, 117 daily wage-basis Sweepers, 119 Old P.T. Sweepers and 85 Baisty working on the Public Health side.

Schedule type C was used for the subordinate staff like para-medicals, sanitary extension educators, dispensers, dressers, nurses, midwives, lady health visitors, vaccinators, malaria workers, sweepers and rat catchers.

As for field study, South Delhi Zone was selected to cover all institutions for depth study. Attempt was made to cover all staff working in South Delhi Zone. All those available (except all class IV staff) were interviewed in addition to the senior officials at the Town Hall. Among respondents from group A, 15 were interviewed at the Town Hall and 5 were interviewed at the zonal level. For the remaining two groups of respondents a detailed breakdown by the type of institutions is given in Table 1.2.

TABLE I.2

Number of Respondents by type of Institutions

Type of Institutions	Schedule B	Schedule C	Total
1. Colony Hospitals	10	25	35
2. Dispensary	4	4	8
3. Urban Health Centre	1	2	3
4. Primary Health Centre	4	2	6
5. Veterinary Hospital	1	1	2
6. Family Planning & M.C.H. Centre	9	16	25
7. Public Health Centre	7	20	27
Total	36	70	106

All the institutions lying within the purview of South Delhi Zone under the administrative management of the Delhi Municipal Corporation were visited and about 121 people, comprising administrators in the Town Hall and zonal level and other categories of staff were met. Of these people, 106 were from South Delhi and 15 from headquarters.

Observation on Implementation of Services

The working of the institutions as included in the South Zone and others included in Table I.3 was observed by constant regular visit from 9 a.m. till 3 p.m. for one and a half year. Every effort was made to stay in each institution from morning till evening to observe programme, procedure and group interaction.

TABLE I.3
Institutions visited outside of South Zone

Sl. No.	Nature of Services	Name of the Institution
1.	Infectious Disease	I.D. Hospital, Kingsway Camp
2.	General Medical Care	Hindu Rao Hospital
3.	Women & Children	Victoria Zanana Hospital
4.	Tuberculosis Treatment	Shyama Prasad Mukherjee Marg T.B. Outdoor Clinic
5.	General Medical Care	Shahdara Hospital
6.	Anti-Malaria Operation	Malaria Eradication Unit, Connaught Circus
7.	Health Education	Health Education Section in City Zone
8.	Outdoor Medical Care	Town Hall Dispensary
9.	M.C.H. & Family Welfare Planning	Basti Harphool Singh Centre

In the final stage, however, visits to the Shahdara and City Zones and several visits to the Town Hall area, which is the heart of the 'walled city' and the T.B. Clinic at the S.P. Mukherjee Marg provided comprehensive material for field study.

The field study was carried out in two stages. At the outset, as mentioned before, ten dispensaries, five family and child welfare centres and outdoor departments of the big hospitals managed by the Delhi Municipal Corporation were visited. These were later revisited. During these visits, discussions were held with the beneficiaries and the officials. Previous experience of the author in various settings as Planning Officer in Community Development Department, West Bengal, Research Officer in the All India Panchayat Parishad and Almoner in London Hospital proved useful. It was of course disheartening to observe the initial indifference of the medical professionals towards a social scientist. However, as the study proceeded, mutual appreciation of information and background and constant endeavour to establish communication removed the difficulties and a good rapport was established.

Having identified the problem areas in the administrative

field, second round of discussions were held with prominent persons in the field. The Department of Health Statistics was visited to collect basic information on the services. The Press and Information Department was also visited for getting additional data. Thereafter, the Chief Medical Officer, Accounts Officer, Deputy Commissioner, Administrative Officer and heads of all sections of the Health Department in the Town Hall and outside were interviewed. Apart from interviewing these persons, discussions with other members of the staff in the respective departments in different echelons were held. Similar discussions with the officials in South Delhi Zone were also carried out between March and June, 1969. During the period of August to November, 1969, the field study was confined to the field executives in the South Delhi Zone. A series of discussions with the Assistant Zonal Commissioner, Zonal Health Officer and the Head Clerk were held. Several trips were also made to South Delhi Zonal Office, Zonal Health Officer's Department to observe the decision-making process and manner of management of services. Interviews with the staff at the lower level were followed by discussions with officials at the Zonal Head Office.

The intensive field study of Zonal Health Department suffers from some limitations. Since the investigator had no direct access to Committee meetings, the deliberations of the Standing Committee or that of the Health Committee could not be personally observed. Analysis of functioning of these bodies, personnel policy and financial procedure are all based on minutes of the meetings and other papers of the Corporation and the narratives provided by the respondents. While the field survey work was going on, there were special occasions, *viz.*, strike in all Government hospitals among junior doctors, strike in Corporation hospitals and strike among the sweepers of the Delhi Municipal Corporation. Later, there was strike among the sweepers in the South Delhi Zone. On all these occasions interviewing the parties involved in the strike provided material for understanding the problem of interrelationships in the health administration.

So far as Health Department of Delhi Municipal Corporation is concerned, the Corporation alone is responsible for administration of health service institutions in Delhi. But as regards health services of the urban metropolis, it is left to different organisations like Central Government and the Union Territory to formulate health policy. Thus, there is no centralised policy-making body for health services in Delhi. Each of the bodies formulates the policy of the institutions working under it. For instance, policy regarding family planning is made by the Family Planning Organization of the Central Government. In the case of the Corporation health agencies, the Standing Committee is the policy-making body within the broad framework of policy and procedure laid down by the Union Government. Each institutional head of the Health Department works under the broad policy laid down by the Corporation and the Health Ministry. It is in view of this that the documents were examined and the interviews with the officials were planned. It was assumed that the study of practices of few institutions managed by the Corporation in South Delhi Zone was a valid means to reveal the policies which govern all the health institutions under Health Department. Moreover, the data are valid to the extent they accurately reflect the management process. However, distortions may occur between the time of behaviour itself and the description of that in final report. Distortion can also result from inaccurate respondent reporting, interviewing process, data processing, analysis and writing the report.

There were quite a few difficulties encountered during the process of data collection. Firstly, the doctors were quite reluctant to extend cooperation to a person from a different discipline. Because of the peculiar secretive nature of local administration, there was persistent resistance to show the files or documents to an outsider. Apart from the health executives the field employees are reluctant to extend cooperation if they find that the researcher has no other status than that of a university student. Secondly, records were not properly maintained and, at times, due to officiousness and secretive nature of administration, it was rather difficult to gather objective data. The Corporation had stopped publishing annual reports since 1963 and some of the directives of the Commissioner were not available in files as they were mostly verbal.

There was reluctance by the doctors to cooperate. The

experience in establishing rapport with the interviewees at the higher echelons, who were scared to part with any information, was frustrating. It took more than one and a half years to build meaningful relationship. Moreover, the nature of job of the health officials dealing with emergency also made it difficult for them to keep up the appointments. Therefore, it used to involve three to four trips to each official. However, due to repeated visits to the Corporation and through personal contact rapport was established at the end of the third year. In the face of the strong feeling of distrust and suspicion prevailing against the politicians, who control the deliberative wing of the Corporation, it was necessary to convince the officials that the data would not be misused for political victimisation. Some of the officials interviewed were rather keen to narrate their problems and express their frustration. However, the staff at lower echelons were very cooperative; they explained in detail all the procedures.

Arrangement of Chapters

The present report is broadly written in three parts, (i) large socio-cultural context, (ii) formal structure and (iii) management process. While the present chapter deals with the introducts on concept and methodology, Chapters II and III present the large socio-cultural context in which the Municipal Corporation organises and carries out its health programmes. We also deal with formal structural aspects of the Municipal Corporation. Chapters IV, V and VI contain description of the formal organisation and various functional aspects of the Health Department which is the main focus of the present enquiry. Chapters VII, VIII and IX dwell on the management process of the Health Department, the personnel, finance and public relations.

The last chapter seeks to examine the working of the department on the assumptions of the social welfare administration and offers some suggestions for future guidance.

CHAPTER II

Ecology and Political Set Up : Delhi

Introduction

Delhi, the seat of the Indian Government, reflects the Indian spirit through the ages as the capital of several dynasties. In 1947, it occupied primate position as the capital of free Republic. The city has seen very rapid expansion in the wake of influx of refugees, migration of population from the far and near States in search of employment. It has been the frequent site of international, political, social, cultural and economic assemblies. The concentration has added to the complex and heterogeneous character of the city.

Physical Set Up

The Union Territory of Delhi is a narrow strip of Indo-Gangetic plain lying between 28.53′ north latitude, 78.90′ and 77.22′ east longitude. It is bounded on the north, west and south by Haryana and on the east by Uttar Pradesh. The Yamuna River flows by the side of its eastern border in a north-south direction, along which the circular Ring Road covers the south-eastern part of the city joining the Ridge Road in west.

22

Distribution Of Population Under Four Local Authorities Of Union Territory Of Delhi

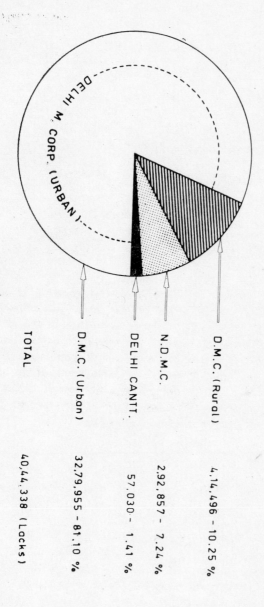

Fig. II.I.

D.M.C. (Rural)   4,14,496 — 10.25 %

N.D.M.C.   2,92,857 — 7.24 %

DELHI CANTT.   57,030 — 1.41 %

D.M.C. (Urban)   32,79,955 — 81.10 %

TOTAL   40,44,338 (Lacks)

Area

The entire area (573 sq. miles) of the Union Territory of Delhi is divided into three main tracts of (a) New Delhi, (b) Delhi Cantonment, (c) Delhi Municipal Corporation.

It may be worthwhile to study the distribution of total area of the Union Territory into various zones as given in 1961 Census (Vol. XIX, p. 13).

TABLE II.1

Distribution of total area of Delhi into various zones

1961 Census Zone	Area in sq. miles	Percentage to total area
Delhi Total	573.00	100.00
Urban Delhi	126.08	22.00
Rural Delhi	446.92	78.00
D.M.C. Urban	92.99	16.23
Zone I—Shahdara	15.25	2.66
Zone II—City Sadar Paharganj	5.00	0.87
Zone III—Karol Bagh-Patel Nagar	6.00	1.05
Zone IV—Civil Lines	10.75	1.88
Zone V—Transferred area	16.00	2.79
Zone VI—South Delhi	24.76	4.32
Zone VII—West Delhi	15.23	2.66
New Delhi	16.50	2.88
Delhi Cantonment	16.59	2.81

The rural area of Union Territory of Delhi comprises 300 villages. Of these, 11 new villages came into existence after 1951. The District Census Handbook 1951 shows that there were only 304 villages in the Union Territory at the time of 1951 Census. The Census Report 1961, however, mentions that 22 villages lost their entity due to urbanisation prior to 1951 Census.

Since the 1961 Census, the area of zones under Delhi Municipal Corporation has been considerably altered with the inclusion of new areas under the Union Territory of Delhi. A number of areas lying to the south of the Transferred Zone have been included in New Delhi South Zone and the rest have gone to the City South Zone. The tide of urbanisation is engulfing more and more rural areas.

Population

The population of the Union Territory of Delhi as recorded in Census 1971 is 40,44,338, which constitutes 0.74% of India's total population. Among the Union Territories, Delhi has the largest concentration of population with 89.75 per cent urban population.

The following statement gives the comparative picture of growth rates of population for the four Census tracts in the two decades 1951-61 and 1961-71.

TABLE II.2

Growth Rate of Population

Union Territory/Census Tract	% Growth rate of population	
	1951-1961	1961-1971
Union Territory of Delhi	+52.44	+52.12
New Delhi Municipal Committee	− 5.35	+11.97
Delhi Cantt.	−11.83	+57.96
Delhi Municipal Corporation (total)	+65.47	+56.48
Delhi Municipal Corporation (Urban)	N.A.	+56.75
Delhi Municipal Corporation (Rural)	N.A.	+54.38

Provisional population totals, Delhi

It may be seen that there was a fall in growth rate of population in the decade 1951-61 in case of New Delhi Municipal Committee (−5.35%) and Delhi Cantt. (−11.83%) while there was an increase in the growth rate of these two towns during 1961-71 by +11.97% and +57.96% respectively.

Literacy

According to Census Directorate, a person is 'literate' if he can both read and write with understanding in any language. Literacy rate of Delhi which was 52.75% at the 1961 Census rose up to 56.65% in 1971. In spite of this increase in the literacy rate, the first ranking position of Delhi in 1961 Census has come down to third in 1971. This is due to the rise in literacy rate in other parts of India.

Socio-Economic Pattern

A few studies on Delhi present some fascinating facts on its socio-economic character as developed in post-independence era. One of the earliest studies made by Bopagamage (1957) showed that 17.3 per cent of Delhi's population lived on Manufacturing and Mining and predominance of service class over others. Gore's (1968) study reveals that Delhi is dominated by the 'service class' as a single profession. Mitra's (1970) study shows how different areas are inhabited by different economic groups, for example, Shahdara, Karol Bagh, Paharganj, being predominantly lower middle class, while South and Central New Delhi and Civil Lines are inhabited by the upper income group. Although the city area has a business class of people, it does not have any impact on the 'elite of the society'. Om Mathur (1968) shows that of the estimated 38,00,000 population of the capital, 75 per cent live in slums under sub-human conditions. Besides, the 17 lakh slum dwellers in the the walled city, a reminiscence of Mughal Delhi and West Delhi, there are about 9 lakh squatters and 200 unauthorised colonies with a population of 1,40,000 and 103 regularised colonies with a population of 3 lakh. The 1961 Census figures indicate that 53.2 per cent of the total population live in one room, 27.2 per cent in two rooms, 9.3 per cent in three rooms, 5.00 per cent in 4 rooms and 4.7 per cent in 5 rooms. About 0.6 per cent have no regular room to live in. Total number of homeless people was recorded as 20,000 in 1971 Census. Urban population in relation to total population of Delhi works out to 89.75 per cent (1971 Census), whereas it was 88.75 per cent (1961 Census) and 82.40 per cent in 1951. Density of population in Delhi on an average is 2,723 square kilometres. Out of every 100 persons, who are supposed to be economically active, 45 form part of the working force. Of the balance of the working force, the Census figures show that 65.6 per cent work in tertiary sector. 1971 provisional Census figures show that 30 per cent of total population of Delhi are economically active. Of this, 50.41 per cent are male and 5.15 per cent female.

On the ecological character of Delhi, Mitra (1970 : 17) reports the concentration of low and middle income group colonies in suburbia of Civil Lines, while the solid rich still occupy the heart of Old Civil Lines. The low and middle (class) income belt then extends to the City area and Karol Bagh in West and Lodi Colony to Ramakrishnapuram, Green Park, Hauz Khas in the South. The Jhuggi or shack town still hugs close to the prosperous areas, but is rapidly being replaced by multi-storeyed colonies and dignified colonies like J.J. Colony. The oldest and most congested area is still the old city area, within the walled Delhi. Within New Delhi Municipal Committee area, New Delhi south of Rajpath is a prosperous area whereas Vinay Nagar, Lodi Road are inhabited by low income groups. Shahdara, on the other hand, is mainly a settlement of industrial workers and also of those who make their living in small factories, interspersed with houses of their entrepreneurs. West Delhi again is an industrial settlement, having its parallel in south of Ring Road, the Okhla Industrial Estate, down to Tughlakabad and Ballabhgarh. Small industries are marked in areas towards Mehrauli beyond Hauz Khas, near Najafgarh and Tilak Nagar. Thus, the Delhi map presents a varied picture of socio-economic groups closely lined up together.

Composition of Delhi population in terms of principal religions in 1961 suggests that the character of the city has gradually changed. The Hindus, proportionately less in 1931 (63 per cent and Muslims 33 per cent of the total population), came up to 84 per cent in 1951-61 (with Muslims between 5.7 per cent in 1951 and 5.9 in 1961 of the total population). Other main religious groups like Sikhs (7.67 per cent), Jains (1.11 per cent), Christians (1.10 per cent) and Buddhists (0.21 per cent) with very small population have showed a steady rate of increase.

Political Set Up

The district of Delhi was constituted by East India Company in 1819 and remained as such with some territorial variation till 1911. In 1857, it became the easternmost Division of

Punjab comprising seven districts of Simla, Ambala, Hissar, Rohtak, Gurgaon and Delhi. The district also contained about 714 villages.

(a) Deputy Commissioner's Delhi

Ultimately in 1912, Delhi became the capital of the country with the transfer of capital of the Indian Empire from Calcutta to Delhi. Through a proclamation issued in October, 1912, the Central Government took over the administration of Delhi district, through the medium of an officer, titled "Deputy Commissioner".

When the announcement was made to make Delhi the capital of the British Government, a portion was carved out, in order to house the new capital. There was thus some reorganisation in which two tehsils of Delhi district, the whole of Sonepat and 280 square miles of Ballabhgarh Tehsil were detached and tagged on to Rohtak and Gurgaon districts respectively. The Tehsil of Delhi and the area under Mehrauli police station were combined to constitute the new province of Delhi. The new province covered an area of 528 square miles with a population of 2,32,837, which has almost increased by 20 times to over 40.44 lakhs in 1971.

After a short period, it was felt necessary to expand the boundaries of the capital a little further. Through a proclamation issued on April 12, 1915, a small area of 45 square miles from the United Provinces, comprising some 65 villages and including the township of Shahdara, was added to the province. Since then the total area of Delhi continues to be 578 square miles.

Since 1912, Delhi has maintained its character as metropolis of India and its system of government has always been designed, bearing this character in view. It was for this reason that Delhi was denied certain powers given to the part 'C' states when Indian Government made it a part 'C' State in 1952.

During 1912-21, three new urban units were created in Delhi, viz., (1) Civil Lines notified area, which had become the temporary seat of the Central Government, (2) Raisina Municipality of the second class in the new capital area, which ultimately became the New Delhi Municipality of the first class and (3) the New Cantonment adjoining the latter municipality on its western side.

According to 1921 Census, Urban Delhi comprised 5 towns —the Red Fort, Delhi Municipality, Civil Lines, New Delhi and New Cantonment. The 1931 Census added Shahdara to the above list of townships.

Functional specialisation, as it exists today, was strictly limited to the four towns where overall control was exercised on individual township basis. Of these, Cantonment and Red Fort areas were military establishments. New Delhi is par excellence a government city. The Civil Lines functioned as the temporary seat of the Imperial Government for a period of 15 years before New Delhi became ready for habitation. Thereafter also, it retained its administrative character by replacing officials of the Central Government by those of the Delhi Administration. Old Delhi remained predominantly commercial.

Greater Delhi consisted of 11 towns. Each of these towns was under the separate and independent jurisdiction of a municipal or notified area town committee. In the aggregate, the area under these local bodies used to be 70,649 acres or 110 square miles.

Historically speaking, Mehrauli, Najafgarh and Narela are very old and small settlements. While Mehrauli and Najafgarh were declared notified area as early as in 1901, Narela became a notified area only in 1919.

(b) Delhi as Chief Commissioner's State

The political status of Delhi as a centrally administered territory continued to be same under both the Government of India Acts of 1919 and 1935. In 1947 after independence, Delhi continued to remain as Chief Commissioner's Province until 1950. On January 26, 1950 with the Constitution of India coming into force, the four-fold categorisation of the States and the Territories was recognised. These were the States included in part A, B, and C and Territories in part D of the First Schedule of the Constitution. Administration of part C States as well as Territories in part D of the First Schedule was made the direct responsibility of the President.

(c) Delhi as Part 'C' State

According to the First Schedule of the Indian Constitution, 1950, in post-independence era, Delhi was categorised as Part C State along with other Union Territories, like Ajmer, Coorg, Himachal Pradesh, Tripura, Manipur, etc.

During the twenties and thirties there have been demands for raising the political status of Delhi and extending its boundaries from time to time. Various conferences and meetings advocated statehood for Delhi. A Committee, popularly known as Pattabhi Committee, was appointed to go into this issue. The Committee unanimously recommended the constitution of a democratic form of government both in Delhi and other part 'C' States. Consequently, the President of India, under Articles 239 and 240 of the Constitution, was empowered to administer these Part 'C' States to such extent as he thought fit through a Chief Commissioner or a Lt. Governor. As a result of the enforcement of the Part 'C' States Act, 1951, Union Government adopted a pattern of representative government in several Part 'C' States, including Delhi. Thus, the Delhi Legislative Assembly came into being on March 17, 1952. It may be mentioned that limited powers had been granted to Part 'C' States, as could be evidenced in the First Schedule of the Constitution. This power was further curtailed in case of Delhi, as could be seen from the proviso to Section 21 of the Part 'C' States Act, 1951.

For instance, Delhi Assembly could not make laws in relation to the following matters : (a) Public Order, (b) Police (c) Offences against law etc.

(d) Delhi as Union Territory

Central Government soon realised that the creation of representative administration at the state level limited overall power enjoyed by the President. Consequently, the States Reorganisation Committee in 1956 recommended direct Central Government administration and introduction of old pattern in Part 'C' States. The Commission came to the conclusion that the democratic experiment in part 'C' States had proved to be costly, and that it was not compensated by administrative efficiency for future development. Therefore, these states should not subsist as separate units. The decisions of the Government were embodied in the States Reorganisation Act, 1956, and the Constitution (Seventh Amendment) Act, 1956. The other Part 'C' States were merged with neighbouring States. It may be mentioned here that in place of former categorisation of Part A, B, C & D States, the Constitution now recognised only two, viz., (i) States and (ii) Union Territories. This resulted in abolition of the Delhi State Assembly on November 1, 1956.

Thus the status of statehood came to an abrupt end making Delhi merely a Union Territory. As the States Reorganisation Commission attached great importance to the needs of national capital, it recommended direct administration for Delhi. Thus the practice of British Government to exclude Delhi from Provincial Government was reiterated.

On assuming the status of Union Territory, Delhi was given an Advisory Council consisting of the Home Minister, Members of Parliament elected from Delhi, the Mayor, the Vice Chancellor of Delhi University, President of the New Delhi Municipal Committee, Inspector General of Police and the Chairman of Industrial Advisory Board. The Chief Commissioner was directly responsible to the Union Government. The Union Government by abolishing Part 'C' States decided to adopt Territories Council Act in 1956. These Territorial Councils had substantial power over local affairs. But Delhi was denied even this privilege, as Union Territories Act was not extended to it.

This "undemocratic" set up of Delhi gave rise to popular dissatisfaction as expressed through various political parties. All local bodies also protested against abolition of Assembly. In response to this agitation, an official committee was appointed to examine the possibility of giving some measure of autonomy to union territories under the chairmanship of Mr. Ashok Sen. The Ashok Sen Committee in its report submitted on June 16, 1972 recommended the introduction of the largest possible measure of autonomy and the association of popular representation at every level.

However, it recognized that central control over territorial bodies in the matter of finance as well as general policy would have to continue. So within a spell of seven years, the policy of withdrawing representative institutions from Union Territories was slackened. Five Union Territories were given a substantial measure of responsible Government in 1963, when the Government of Union Territories Act was passed. But Delhi was not given any legislature. The amended Article 239A followed generally the provision of Article 240 of Indian Constitution, as it stood before the reorganisation of States. The amendment resulted in the creation of three groups of Union Territories, with limited Legislative Assembly to forge a compromise between various contending forces. Delhi became a distinct class by conceding to its peculiar position as national capital.

It can, however, be mentioned that although the Union Territories Act gives considerable measure of autonomy to the Union Territories, it does not take away anything from the ultimate constitutional responsibility of the President and Parliament. According to Delhi Administration Act, 1966, Delhi has been accorded the present Metropolitan Council, with a 'de facto' status of an Assembly. In this context it may be stated that Delhi Administration (Business) Rules, 1966, framed under Section 29 of Delhi Administration Act, 1966, the Administrator has been asked to keep the Central Government fully posted with certain "reserved" matters.

Metropolitan Council

A certain degree of autonomy was introduced in Delhi, corresponding to the special status of national capital by giving a Metropolitan Council to Delhi on September 7, 1966. The administration of the Union Territory of Delhi today vests in the President acting through an Administrator, designated as Lt. Governor. In order to give representative character to the administrative set up, a Metropolitan Council consisting of 61 members, of whom 56 are elected from territorial constituencies and 5 are nominated, has been created. At present 50 members are elected from Municipal Corporation areas, five from New Delhi Municipal Committee and one from Cantonment area. The Council is presided over by a Chairman elected from amongst the members of the Council. However, the Metropolitan Council has no legislative powers (Delhi Administration Act, 1966).

As at present constituted, the Metropolitan Council is essentially an advisory body and for that reason has a recommendatory character. The main purpose of constituting the Metropolitan Council was to associate representatives of the people with Delhi Administration.

Such being the character of Delhi's Council, people and political leaders always felt that they have been denied of a responsible government. Administrative Reforms Commission in 1970 recommended that with a view to giving greater political respectability to the Metropolitan Council, it will function in a manner similar to a legislature. Parliament and the Union Government may agree to forego their right to intervene in matters falling in transferred list. It further recommended that the Metropolitan Council should constitute a number of Standing Committees, each of them presided over by an Executive Councillor.

Executive Council

Section 27 of the Delhi Administration Act, 1966, provides that there shall be an Executive Council, consisting of not more than four members and one of whom shall be designated as the Chief Executive Councillor to assist and advise the Administrator. Apparently, it looks like a Council of Members. The responsibilities of the Administrator are grouped into two categories—one, the 'reserved' category with regard to which the Administrator can function in his discretion, and the other 'transferred' category, with regard to which the Administrator functions with the assistance and advice of the Council.

The historical development of Delhi's political set up as given above indicates that, truly speaking, no single political approach has so far been permitted to continue for a reasonable time to get consolidated and yield results. The States Reorganisation Commission, 1955 and the Administrative Reforms Commission, in its report on the administration of Union Territories, have adopted conflicting approaches in their recommendations. The most remarkable distinction among these

Committee reports was in regard to the constitution and conti-
nuance of Delhi Municipal Corporation.[1]

The States Reorganisation Commission said, "Municipal
autonomy in the form of Corporation would appear to be the
most appropriate method of meeting and reconciling the broad
requirements of the national Government as well as the local
needs and wishes of the people." The Administrative Reforms
Commission has, however, criticised the multiplicity of
political authorities in Delhi and recommended that the Corporation may be abolished and its municipal functions transferred to the enlarged Metropolitan Council. It states : "With
the reorganisation of the Metropolitan Council and the
enlargement of its jurisdiction, the Delhi Municipal Corporation may be abolished. Thereafter, the Metropolitan Council
will be responsible for municipal administration throughout
the Territory, except in areas falling within the jurisdiction of
New Delhi Municipal Committee and Delhi Cantonment."

Municipal Corporation of Delhi

It may be of historical interest to note that in 1863, by a
notification issued under the Punjab Municipal Act, Delhi
Municipality was created to look after public health and convenience. It became a first class Municipality in 1881. In
accordance with the recommendation of the States Reorganisation Commission, the Delhi Municipal Corporation was constituted on April 7, 1958, to bring about a consolidated and
comprehensive municipal administration of the city. The
Corporation has jurisdiction over the entire Union Territory
of Delhi except for the areas falling within the administrative
control of N.D.M.C. and Delhi Cantonment Board. The
Cantonment Board is responsible for functions normally assigned to a local government institution in charge of municipal
administration of the army habitation. Though, New Delhi
Municipal Committee continues to function, its jurisdiction has
been reduced from 32 to 16.50 square miles.

A unique characteristic of Delhi Municipal Corporation is

1. The following chapters are all devoted to the D.M.C.

that, it has a large number of villages, as much as 258 in number. These rural areas have panchayats for their local administration, under the Delhi Panchayat Raj Act, 1954. Delhi has two tiers of Panchayat administration, i.e., Panchayat at village level and Panchayat Samiti at block level. The functions of the Gram Panchayat are promotion of agriculture, animal husbandry, cooperative farming, cottage industries, fisheries and forests. Panchayat Samiti on the other hand is meant to advise the administration (and the Corporation if it so decides) on development schemes, preparation and execution of development plans, approval of Panchayat budget, coordination of plans covering more than one Panchayat, disbursement of loans and grants as may be placed at the disposal of the Samiti and any other functions which may be arranged by the Administration or Corporation.

Till the setting up of Municipal Corporation, Greater Delhi, as it was called, had eleven towns within its geographical area as stated before. There was also the Delhi District Board to look after the needs of rural areas.

The Corporation took over the functions previously entrusted to all the local bodies excluding New Delhi Municipal Committee and the Cantonment Board. Delhi State Electricity Board, Delhi Road Transport Authority and Delhi Joint Water and Sewage Board were all included in the administrative purview of the Corporation.

The Corporation consists of 100 elected Councillors and six Aldermen, elected by the Councillors. The Corporation is headed by a Mayor, who is annually elected. He is entitled to have an access to all records of the Corporation. Municipal Corporation functions through six Statutory Committees, i.e., the Standing Committee, the Delhi Electricity Supply Committee, Delhi Water Supply and Sewage Disposal Committee, Rural Areas Committee, Delhi Transport Committee and Education Committee.

The Delhi Municipal Corporation Act is mainly based on the scheme of Bombay Corporation Act. It separates deliberative from executive wing. The chief executive authority is the Municipal Commissioner. According to 1971 Census, about 81.10 per cent of total population of Delhi live in D.M.C. (Urban) and 10.25 per cent in D.M.C. (Rural).

Decentralisation of Administration

In December, 1958, while the erstwhile Municipal Committees were dissolved according to the first schedule of the D.M.C. Act 1957, the local offices still continued to remain as civic centres, performing limited day-to-day functions and attending to the public inconveniences. But the major policy decisions about building plans or water connections remained centrally administered. This was causing delay and inconvenience to the public. In 1962, an Ad Hoc Committee, appointed to study the decentralised executive functions of the Corporation, observed that the administration suffered from over-centralisation. Ad Hoc Committee also pointed out that the undefined responsibilities of the Zonal Officer, who was the technical head of the Zonal Office and the Zonal Assistant Collector were creating great tension in their personal relationship thereby defeating the very purpose of the administration. Consequently, in 1965, the Corporation adopted decentralisation in its administrative system. Thus, as it has been discussed before, it is evident that the Corporation works through its Committee system and decentralised zonal administrative system.

New Delhi Municipal Committee

New Delhi Municipal Committee covers an area of approximately 16.50 square miles comprising 7.24% of total population of Delhi. The boundary line of New Delhi Municipal Committee is defined in the first schedule to the D.M.C. Act, 1957. The N.D.M.C. is governed by the Punjab Municipal Act, 1911. The Municipal Committee is accountable to the Lt. Governor, who can give any directive to it. The present Committee is constituted of 11 nominated members, out of which one is President, four officials and six non-officials who are appointed by the Lt. Governor of the Union Territory of Delhi.

Cantonment Board

The administration of the Cantonment area is at present entrusted to the Delhi Cantonment Board as per Cantonment

Act, 1924. The functions of the Cantonment Board are identical to any other Cantonment Board in India, i.e., civic amenities.

The Board consists of seven nominated members and seven elected members. The ultimate control of the Board vests in General Officer Commanding-in-Chief. Administrative Reforms Commission, 1969 advocated that the Cantonment Board should have its representatives on Metropolitan Council and other statutory bodies. According to 1971 Census, about 1.41 per cent of total population of Delhi reside in the Cantonment area.

Delhi Development Authority

Delhi Development Authority is a statutory body created under the provisions of the Delhi Development Authority Act, 1957. It is responsible for the implementation of the Master Plan and for promoting and securing planned development of Delhi. It is also in charge of developing new colonies and public buildings. It consists of Lt. Governor as ex-officio Chairman, a whole-time Vice Chairman, two whole-time members, appointed by the Central Government for Finance and Accounts and Engineering, three nominees of the Central Government and the Commissioner of Delhi Municipal Corporation.

The foregoing description shows the developments of political status of Delhi with its peculiar characteristics. The jurisdiction of the Corporation along with the New Delhi Municipal Committee and Cantonment Board is coextensive with the boundary of the Union Territory of Delhi. Its status as Capital warrants, (a) special provision and maintenance of municipal services and public utilities. There are also the matters of direct concern to the Government of India. Expansion of Government structures, offices and newly developed 338 residential colonies pose a heavy strain on its services. The rural part of Delhi Corporation area poses some special problems which are not found in any other Corporation. (b) Delhi Corporation area extends to 512 square miles, out of which only 99 square miles is urban; with 34 lakhs of population and about 3.4 lakhs scattered over 300 rural abadis and township of

Greater Delhi.   The Corporation spends about Rs. 150 lakhs
per annum in the rural area against a revenue of about Rs. 5
lakhs to meet its liabilities. (c) Delhi Municipal Corporation
from its inception in 1958 suffers from the hangover of the
problem of integrating the municipal services of the erstwhile
seven municipalities, with the functions of the District Board
and those of the State Government.

The Corporation is also entrusted with the special responsibility of providing services in the areas developed by the Delhi
Development Authority. Like any other Metropolitan Government, Delhi is also confronted with the problem of preserving
and promoting the health of its citizens. The normal difficulties faced in seeking solution to this problem have been further
complicated by the special socio-political characteristics and
the rapid increase in population as indicated above.

Against this background of the city, we shall examine the
formal structure of the Delhi Municipal Corporation Health
Department and the mode of its operation.

CHAPTER III

Policy and Legal Framework for Health Services

A service programme is evolved within the policy framework of the state. The nature of the activities and their operation is regulated by the legal framework. In view of this it is desirable that we discuss these aspects before we go to examine the nature of programmes in the area of health services undertaken by the Corporation. We shall deal with both the national and local policy framework within which health programme has been organised.

Health is the science of preventive and curative medicine as practised by the Government. The recognised functions include seven standard services, *viz.*, vital statistics, communicable disease control, environmental sanitation, public health laboratory work, protection of maternity, infant and child hygiene, public health education and curative services. Most of the health legislations are based upon the idea that prevention and control of communicable diseases is the first and foremost duty of the health authorities.

Historical Background

Historically speaking the indigenous system of medicine was well developed in this country. The most important of

38

these are the Ayurveda and the Unani system. The former was developed in the early historical period by ancient Hindu physicians like Charaka and it was by and large followed by the Hindus. The Unani system, on the other hand, was developed by the Mohammedan rulers of India and was generally followed by the Muslims. The Allopathic system, which is relatively new to this country, was introduced by the Europeans.

A more elaborate system of public health was introduced under the British rule. In order to evolve the system a host of legislations was enacted by the British rulers. The first among the laws was the Quarantine Act, 1825. This was intended to enable the Government to segregate the people suffering from communicable diseases, from contact with the troops.

A Public Health Committee was appointed in 1864 for surveying the public health needs of Bengal, Madras and Bombay presidencies. The Birth and Death Registration Act was enacted in 1873, to have a record of births and deaths. A Plague Commission was appointed in 1886. In the same year an important decision was taken to establish local bodies under the Local Bodies Act of 1886. Consequently, the responsibility for the health and sanitation of the people was entrusted to the local authorities. About this time the Vaccination Act of 1880 was passed. Seven years later, the Epidemic Diseases Act, 1887 was passed. This body of legislations provided the basic framework for the growth of public health policy and its administration.

However, there was a change in the broad policy frame when the provincial and later state legislations were enacted. This came in the wake of devolution of authority from the centre to the states under the Minto-Morley and Montague-Chelmsford constitutional reforms. Under the latter reforms, the subject of public health and medical relief was included in the transferred subjects of the state list. However, the Central Government still retained a considerable degree of control over the matters relating to health. With the introduction of provincial autonomy, under the Government of India Act, 1935, the ministries in the States were made wholly responsible for health policy and administration. During this period an important landmark was the Public Health Act, 1939, which could be considered a model of its kind even today. Drugs Act was enacted in 1940 as a Central legislation.

With the outbreak of the Second World War the normal constitutional system was disrupted and normalcy was not restored until after 1947, when the country was partitioned. However, an important event during the forties was the appointment of the Health Survey and Development Committee, known as Bhore Committee, named after its Chairman, Sir Joseph Bhore. This Committee submitted its report in 1946, on the future set up of health administration in India, both at the Centre and in the States.

Centre and State Relations

As for the inter-governmental relations, the distribution of responsibilities between the Centre and the States was very much blurred till the second decade of the current century. In 1922, in the wake of the Montague-Chelmsford Reforms Act, the devolution policy of the Government entrusted health, sanitation and vital statistics to the provincial governments. The Centre still retained its right to advise and make suggestions. The Centre had the upper hand to direct the course of action of the provincial governments. It seemed that this make-shift arrangement was to allow medical relief and public health system to evolve itself without much interference from the Central Government. An effective control from the Central Government was being exercised by placing Indian Medical Service Officers in charge of medical and health administration of districts and even of all hospitals and medical institutions of every category. The 1935 Act, later on, classified the entire field of health activities of the government into 3 categories. Central Government's responsibilities included: (i) International health and post-quarantine, (ii) Inter-State quarantine, (iii) Medical research, (iv) Higher Medical Education, (v) Administration of Central Agencies, and (vi) Medical and Health administration of the areas directly administered by the Centre. The State was otherwise responsible for all health and medical activities. There was also a Concurrent List in which both States and the Central Government had the power to legislate upon.

However, there are certain provisions in the Constitution which are significant from the standpoint of health policy. For example, Article 47 of the Directive Principles of the Indian Constitution points out the basic responsibility of the State towards the promotion of health and standard of living as follows :

"The State shall regard the raising of the level of nutrition and standard of living of its people and improvement of public health as among its primary duties and in particular, the State shall endeavour to bring about prohibition of the consumption, except for medical purposes, of intoxicating drinks or drugs which are injurious to health."

Article 47 of the Constitution further states :

"The State shall, within the limits of its economic capacity and development, make effective provision for securing the right to work, to education and to public assistance in cases of unemployment, old age, sickness and disablement, and in other cases of undeserved want."

Indian Constitution 1950 provided for a statutory Central Council of Health to discuss matters of dispute over subjects in the concurrent list, and, also to bring about coordination in policy and action with respect to health subjects. Central Health Council has been meeting over the years together, taking very important decisions. Establishment of Central Council of Health, however, provided a forum for discussion of medical and health matters related to the country as a whole.

It is significant to note that the administration of health, education and welfare was trifurcated and health assumed independent status only in 1945. With the formation of Central Council of Health in 1947, at the Centre, to coordinate the health activities of the country, and the publication of the Bhore Committee Report (1947), like Dawson Committee in U.K., "Health" assumed a considerable importance in the Government administration. The concept of a primary health centre with comprehensive health care for a population of 40,000 was conceived. The acceptance of the ideology of Welfare State with all its ramifications further stipulated the streamlining of organisational and procedural system of health administration in India.

Health Policy

Since 1945 till today, a number of Committees were formed to advise on the health policy of India. All these Committees from time to time tried to review the health position of the country and suggested integrated system of health administration. The Health Survey and Development Committee Report 1946, among other things, reviewed the health administration pattern in the country as a whole, and specially that of the local area. It advocated the adoption all over the country of the pattern of legislation embodied in the Public Health Act of Madras, 1939. Section 127 of the Act provided that every municipality shall earmark 30 per cent of its income from other sources than government grant for public health in its local area. The Madras Act empowers the provincial Health Officers to recommend to the local health authorities the particular administrative directions in health measures. The Bhore Committee Report suggested a unified health authority for the whole district. It advocated for the constitution of the District Health Board as an elected body. In case of large municipalities/corporations, it is expected that they should be able to maintain and develop their own health services and they need not be brought under the District Health Organisation. Taking into consideration the special status of Delhi, the Committee further suggested a separate pattern of health administration for Delhi area (see Appendix A.1). It advocated the urban and rural health centre concept (1946 : 303-313).

Evolution of Health Centre Concept

The first publication which set forth the regionalised health centre concept in detail was by Lord Dawson, father of the Penn Report in 1920, in post First World War period. There was realisation in England during that period that the health services must drastically be improved with equalization of opportunity for all. This special Governmental Commission in England suggested that comprehensive care units be established on regional patterns around hospitals, to ensure maximum utilisation of resources and personnel without duplication. But the recommendation of the Dawson Commission was quickly kept aside. The English sentiment was so much conventional that even when the National Health Services were introduced after 20 years, the preventive side was made the responsibility of the local government and the medical care that of the Central Government without any integration of the two services. Even the popularly known Guillebaud Committee Report (1958) did not suggest any improvement on the public health services.

Bhore Committee Report, 1946

Bhore Committee Report, like Dawson Report in England, besides giving an account of the health situation of India, suggested some revolutionary policy for health administration in India. Some of the relevant recommendations, besides those of local bodies, are as follows :

1. Medical and Public Health Services should be totally tax supported and medical personnel should be salaried.
2. Priority should be given to rural need so as to provide primary health centres for each 10 to 20 thousand population regionalized around secondary centres with 650-bed hospitals, again regionalised around district hospital with 2,500 beds.
3. Curative and preventive services to be integrated with greater emphasis on prevention.
4. Municipal Corporation should be vested with local health responsibility.

In 1947 India became independent. Planning Commission was established in 1950 for reconstructing India's socio-economic development. Planning in India was intended to promote rapid rise in the standard of living of the people, by efficient exploitation of natural resources of the country, increasing production and offering opportunities to all for employment. A Health Division was created in the Planning Commission.

Report of the Committee constituted for Model Public Health Act

In 1955 the Committee for Model Public Health Act in its report endorsed the Bhore Committee's suggestion to proceed on the lines of the Madras Public Health Act, 1939. It dwelt on the duty of local authority on maintenance of public health and sanitation.

It further reiterated that health scheme should be prepared by the local authority prior to submitting it to the Central Government. A special committee was constituted in 1958 to find out ways and means to control smallpox in India. It is, however, interesting to note that none of these committees took a total view of the health problem of India. They all tried to take telescopic view of the problem without considering the total health needs. Besides, large part of their work remained mainly paper work which did not have any impact on the total health administration.

Health Centre Manuals

Health services in India were further enriched through a series of health centre manuals about health centre operations (Colonel Barkat Narain and Dr. P.R. Dutt). They were ideal compilations on the role of doctors in that period. Soon it was revealed that the goal was too high to be achieved.

Health Planning

In post-independence era, India took up planning as per Resolution of March, 1950, "to promote a rapid rise in the standard of living of the people by efficient exploitation of the resources of the country, increasing production and offering opportunities to all for employment in the service of the community." Planning Commission was formed with a health cell attached to it. Broad objectives of the health planning were also formulated on implementation of the suggestions of the Bhore Committee Report. The broad objectives of the health programme during all three first Five Year Plans have been to control and eradicate communicable diseases, to provide curative and preventive health services in rural areas through establishment of a primary health centre in each community development block and training of medical personnel. The reorganisation of dispensaries on urban side was also to some extent considered necessary. Bhore Committee Report urged the need for urban health centres in big cities. The Planning Commission soon realised the impracticability of implementing the Bhore Committee recomendations. The problem was to decide between qualitative service and extension of service.

The Mudaliar Committee (1961) emphasised strengthening of the existing 52,000 health centres in India and integration of health services for proper implementation of the plans. In the Third Five Year Plan period no rigid system of priority was fixed except introducing the extension approach in the family planning programme. In the Fourth Five Year Plan, the programme for expansion of public health facilities has been set within the framework of the long-term target suggested by the Health Survey and Planning Committee, popularly known as Mudaliar Committee. Stress was laid on training of basic health workers and other categories of medical personnel. In 1962, the Environmental Hygiene Committee reiterated the need of environmental sanitation as a basic prerequisite of a healthy community.

In family planning, the operational goal, for reducing the birth rate to 25 per thousand as against the prevailing 40 per thousand, is to be achieved by creating facilities for 90% of the married population of India by (i) group acceptance of small sized family, (ii) personal knowledge about family planning methods and (iii) ready availability of supplies and services. During Fourth Plan period family planning found its place as a programme of highest priority.

The Chadha Committee (1963) and Mukherjee Committee (1962) stressed the need for basic health. Chadha Committee suggested one basic health worker for every 15,000 population against 10,000 in rural areas under the supervision of one Inspector for every five basic health workers. It was meant to take up the integrated health services for malaria control and smallpox eradication in urban areas. But none of these reports gave a clear indication whether family planning should also be integrated with the total health plan. Secondly, it did not spell out whether the basic health worker had to work in isolation or in cooperation with people's institutions. Thirdly, the technical and administrative factors involved in integrating the maintenance phase or consolidation phase of different schemes stipulate careful determination. All these committees, except Bhore and Mudaliar Committees, were fragmentary in their approach as they looked into specific problems only. The World Health Organisation and United Nations Children's Emergency Fund, on the other hand, while working in health field through their projects, have been trying to develop the basic health worker concept in the total development of health services.

Organisational Set Up—Centre

During the British period, the technical organisation at the Centre was under the Director General of Medical Services, who was the principal medical adviser to the Government of India, in the Department of Health, Education and Lands. He was also the head of the Indian Medical Service and of the India Medical Department. He was assisted by Public Health Commissioner in public health matters. In the provinces the head of the medical administration was the Inspector General of Civil Hospitals. The remarkable feature of health set up at the district level was the appointment of a whole-time District Public Health Advisory Committee to function as adviser to the provincial and local Government on the needs of the medical care of the institutions.

The Royal Commission of Public Health for Troops in 1859 suggested the extension of public health measures to civil population leading to the enactment of Town Improvements Bill (1871) and Local Funds Act. In 1870, by financial decentralisation resolution of Lord Mayo, education, sanitation, medical charity and public works became the responsibility of local Government.

Provision of medical relief devolved on local authorities. But slender finance of the local authorities did not permit them to make adequate provision. It remained only on paper. Creation of local bodies in 1888, to provide the general sanitation of the areas, is the aftermath of the famous resolution of Lord Ripon on Local Self Government in India. In 1884, as a consequence of the policy enunciated by Lord Ripon, the District Municipalities Act was passed.

Set Up in Delhi

The Delhi Municipal Committee started its recorded activities since December, 1962, according to Title Act XXV of 1850 and Improvement of Towns Act. Act IV of 1873, Act XIII of 1884, Act XX of 1891 and Act III of 1911 were other successive enactments all of which led to gradual evolution of local self government in Delhi. Health Department of the Municipal Committee was created following the Plague Commission Report in 1904, in the wake of outbreak of plague epidemic in Delhi. The administrative control of health services was under the District Civil Surgeon in the whole Delhi area. The Dufferin Hospital (1891-93), the Victoria Zenana, Bara Hindu Rao and Infectious Diseases Hospitals and a group of dipensaries in Paharganj, Sadar Bazar and Kashmere Gate were developed for medical relief, during late nineties. By and large, the general sanitation, regulation of housing, purity of food and the vital statistics became the responsibility of the local authorities. The Delhi District Board maintained dispensaries at Shahdara, Mehrauli, Najafgarh and Narela.

In spite of all these enactments and resolutions on local self government the general level of health administration by the local bodies was low firstly due to inadequate finances to maintain qualified staff and secondly, the elected Chairman sometimes found himself powerless to enforce law against vested interests in the absence of any authority from the Director of Public Health except in case of epidemics. Except in Madras, which had combined legislative and executive authority and transferred all power to the local health officer, no other Municipal Committee made any special headway. Delhi was then divided into (i) Delhi City, (ii) New Delhi, (iii) Delhi Notified Area (Civil Lines), (iv) New Cantonments and (v) Rural Circles; each area, with the exception of the Rural Circles, had its own Health Officer and staff. Health Officer

was under the administrative control of an Indian Medical
Service Officer.

The Delhi City itself was divided into 16 wards for the
sanitary administration. As regards the sanitary staff, the
Delhi Municipal Committee, with 2½ lakhs of population,
had two Chief Sanitary Inspectors, 6 Sanitary Circle Inspectors, 40 Daroghas, 2 Sewer Gang Inspectors, 350 Road
Sweepers, 388 Bhisthis, 55 Dalao Chowkidar, 71 Latrine
Sweepers and 130 Sweepers on miscellaneous work. The New
Delhi area, with its one-seventh population (32,000 people and
40 square miles) of Delhi City, had one Health Officer, one
Sanitary Superintendent (European), two Sanitary Inspectors
(one European and one Indian), four Sanitary Daroghas and
nine Jamadars by dividing the areas into 4 wards. New Delhi
being the site of civilians and bureaucrats, received special care
in regard to its cleanliness. Till 1926, the Public Health Staff
of New Delhi area was under the.Public Works Department of
the Delhi Administration. The Sanitary Engineer of the Public
Works Department was in charge of the maintenance of sewers,
drains and water supply.

The Civil Lines area, inhabited by the Viceroy and the
Commander-in-Chief, with about 17,000 persons, had one
Health Officer, one Sanitary Inspector, one Sanitary Superin-
tendent (European), four Daroghas as health staff. The Civil
Lines Health Department was under the municipality and was
financed by a Government grant of Rs. 2 lakhs per annum.
All the bye-laws of the Punjab Municipal Act 1911 and Central
Health Laws were applicable to these municipalities. The
Cantonment area had their bye-laws under the Cantonment
Act. It had a part-time I.M.S. Officer, a qualified Inspector
and menial staff for public health administration.

In the New Delhi area there was one Welfare Centre with
a Health Visitor. Three more Maternity and Child Welfare
Centres were run in different parts of the city, adjoining the
hospitals. The earliest attempt to provide medical care to
women and children was started in Delhi in 1918 by opening
Lady Reading Health School and Lady Chelmsford All India
League for Maternity and Child Welfare in 1928.

The Delhi Municipal Committee had staff for rat destruction,
vaccination, slaughter house, marketing, maternity and infant

welfare, vital statistics and office work. The Maternity and Infant Welfare Staff working in the Municipal Committee under a female Medical Superintendent had four Welfare Centres, namely, (1) Nicholson Road, (2) Jhandewalan, (3) Kundewalan and (4) near Jama Masjid, with a staff consisting of junior and senior Health Visitor, a nurse and small menial staff. The drinking water was obtained from the joint water board. But the filtered water was not available for the whole town. The scavenging and refuse work were done mostly on contract basis.

The rest of the Delhi province except Delhi Municipal Committee was under the District Board. It had scattered rural area with very poor sanitary conditions and no Health Officer. In larger villages, which had government dispensaries, the Sub-Assistant Surgeon used to supervise the sanitation of the village. The vital statistics were kept by village headmen and most of the deaths were recorded as fever cases. However, the report on Health Organisations in British India (1928 : 90-97) indicates that there were some activities for infectious diseases control, as mostly the cases were imported to the city. There was an anti-plague gang consisting of 2 Assistant Surgeons, 2 Compounders, 8 mates and 35 coolies, who travelled about the area, trapping and batting rats and giving anti-plague inoculations. The gang used to visit houses and persuade people to get vaccinated in case of cholera and smallpox. All these statements suggest that there was great disparity in provision of health services in different parts of Delhi. The areas inhabited by "civilians had better standard of health administration than those inhabited by natives."

In 1945, the post of the Director General of Health Services for Delhi was created integrating public health and medical care.

Delhi also enacted various legislations to promote health and welfare of the people. Of these legislations in Delhi, the significant ones are the Dentists Act 1948, Drugs Act 1940, Delhi Nursing Home Act 1953, Delhi Anatomy Act 1953, Delhi Pharmacy Act 1948 and Drugs & Magic Remedies Act 1954. These Acts were promulgated in Punjab and extended to Delhi. They continue to be extended throughout the whole Union Territory of Delhi.

In 1946, the Delhi Municipal Committee assumed democratic status to elect its own Chairman and assumed further responsibilities in environmental sanitation. But the Public Health Services in Delhi faced a heavy strain of influx of refugees in 1947. The change-over of the total administrative set up in post-partition period brought a heavy strain on the government, posing a challenge to the normal activities of the Municipal Corporation.

In 1952, political status of Delhi had another leap conferring statehood on Delhi. Thus the erstwhile health institutions managed by the local government were transferred to the Delhi Administration.

With the Prevention of Food Adulteration Act 1954-55, the Health Department of the Delhi Municipality was given added authority to punish the culprits in deviant cases.

In 1955 Medical and Health Reorganisation Committee, popularly known as Gilder Committee, was set up to suggest streamlining of the health administration for the State of Delhi. The Contributory Health Service Scheme for Government employees in Delhi was instituted in 1954.

While the area of the Union Territory of Delhi of 573 sq. miles continued to be unchanged since 1950, that of the Municipal Corporation has grown from 25.6 to 93 sq. miles with incorporation of Delhi Civil Lines, Shahdara, Red Fort, Narela, Mehrauli and Najafgarh. New Delhi Municipal Committee shrank by little over half (16.6 sq. miles) and Delhi Cantonment by 1961 about 2.4 square miles from 19 sq. miles, thus swelling Corporation's urban area. The Health Department of the Union Territory was soon reorganised. Public health activities along with the control of seven hospitals and health centres, 17 dispensaries and the Leper Home were transferred to the newly emerged Municipal Corporation.

The present Municipal Corporation of Delhi came into being in May, 1958, to carry out the municipal functions of Union Territory of Delhi. The erstwhile health departments managed by different constituent local bodies were integrated into one health department of the Corporation which undertook the responsibility of all the health programmes for the entire city.

In 1958, an Army Medical Officer was appointed on deputation, to take charge of the newly constituted Health Department of the Corporation. He was looking after all the hospitals under the Corporation until 1962. He was deprived of administrative control over big hospitals of the Corporation after 1962. In 1969, a new Health Officer, on deputation from the Army Medical Corps, joined as Municipal Health Officer with enhanced status. He took over control of all big hospitals except Hindu Rao and Silver Jubilee Hospitals.

In the process Malaria Control, Tuberculosis Unit and the Epidemiology Unit were added to the department. After two years of working, Epidemiology Unit had to be closed down due to financial difficulty. In 1965, the Family Planning Unit was added to the Maternity and Child Health Section of the Corporation. For effective administration decentralisation and devolution of administrative power zonal administration was introduced in 1965.

Health Situation in Delhi

To ascertain the health situation of the population of Delhi, we may refer to (i) the Demographic and health conditions and (ii) Health Services in metropolis.

The available information on the general health of the population is based on the records of the Central Government Health Services studies, Census Reports and Corporation health data. In any study of the problems of metropolitan city we have to take into consideration the socio-economic characteristics of the predominantly immigrant population, degree of urbanisation and industrialisation. An attempt has been made here to present an overall picture of the population in the metropolis, although it is well recognised that wide variation in socio-economic conditions of different sections of the population would also be reflected in their health.

Demographic Character

The demographic growth of Delhi reflects the world pattern of the present century till 1950, showing a slow growth till 1931, watershed till 1941 and very fast in the last two decades (A. Mitra : 17-18). It registered 36.2 per cent growth in

1941-51. From a little over 2 lakhs in 1901, the urban Delhi grew by slow degrees to a mere $4\frac{1}{2}$ lakhs in 1931, but took a sudden stride to 7 lakhs in 1941 and more than doubled itself to 1.53 million in 1951 and to 2.4 million in 1961. The estimate of population for 1981 was 5 million, but by 1966, it has already reached 4.044 million as per 1971 Census. According to Census 1961, Delhi with the highest percentage of urban population in the whole of India is comparable to any Western metropolitan city like New York, Washington D.C., London, Paris and Tokyo.

Density

The fastest area to grow in Delhi during the decade was West Delhi (more than five times over again as in 1951) followed by Shahdara (more than twice again as in 1951); Karol Bagh, Patel Nagar, Civil Lines, Subzimandi, New Delhi and Transferred Area, each grew by more than half as much again as in 1951. City Sadar Paharganj grew by more than 7 per cent in 1961, while population declined in Delhi Cantonment area. The density of population for the Delhi Territory in 1961 was 1,791 per square kilometre and has now reached 2,723 as per Census 1971. But the areas like Sadar Bazar, Paharganj and Chandni Chowk have a density of 55,256 persons per square kilometre which is close to double the density of Calcutta Municipal Area and more than six times the density of Greater Bombay. Karol Bagh and Patel Nagar have a density of 20,804 per square kilometre, which is nearly 2-3 times the average density of Calcutta Municipal Corporation and more than double the density of Greater Bombay. These two zones can be counted as the world's highest density areas (Census 1961).

Mortality

Two indices have been examined to ascertain the health status, viz., infant mortality and the general mortality and birth rate of the population in metropolis. As is well known, a problem in such studies arises from the deficiencies in the

registration system, particularly, in areas facing rapid population growth and population shift.

Infant Mortality Rate

The records show that Delhi had always high trend in
infant mortality. The study indicates that from 1964-65 on-
wards there has been an increase in the infant mortality rate
up to the year 1967-68, as shown in Table III.1.

TABLE III.1
Mortality Rate in Delhi during 1962-69

Year	Birth Rate	Death Rate	Infant Mortality	Maternal Death
1962-63	29.34	8.28	71.42	1.07
1963-64	28.48	8.56	61.45	1.71
1964-65	28.3	7.3	47.16	1.9
1965-66	29.50	8.09	65.17	2.9
1966-67	30.4	7.9	62.8	0.19
1967-68	30.8	8.1	64.0	0.49
1968-69	30.6	8.0	66.0	0.40

Source :   Statistical Unit, Health Department, D.M.C. 1970

The rates of infant mortality in these two periods are 47
and 66 per thousand births respectively. Whether this recorded increase is attributable to better registration system is not
clear. However, a part of this increase could as well be due to
the growth of population as indicated earlier. In contrast,
the infant mortality rates in Western countries in 1930 were as
follows: U.S.—85; Canada—89; U.K.—60; Ireland 68;
Australia—42; New Zealand—34. It is, however, evident that
the present rate of infant mortality in Delhi is comparable to
Western countries in 1930.

General Mortality

The general mortality rate of Delhi has been recorded to
be 8.28 to 8 per thousand (as shown in Table III.1) which is
considerably less than the all-India incidence of 46.4 per
thousand. Although the area-wise distribution of mortality

rate is not available, statistical information in respect of the
infectious diseases like enteric fever indicates that death rate is
the highest in the concentrated Corporation area.

TABLE III.2

**Mortality due to infectious and parasitic diseases in Delhi
during the years 1962-68**

Year	Cholera	Small-pox	Fever	Dysentery, Diarrhoea	Respira-tory Dise-ases T.B.	Other Cases
1962-63	—	207	3,392	846	4,324	12,800
1963-64	—	36	4,325	888	2,899	16,547
1964-65	5	69	4,316	813	8,586	14,256
1965-66	2	68	3,899	874	5,305	14,153
1966-67	1	110	3,953	909	9,809	15,820
1967-68	2	30	3,085	867	2,999	17,845
1968-69	4	40	3,906	868	2,881	18,846
1969-70	6	95	3,085	800	4,881	19,024

Source : Statistical Unit of Health Department, D.M.C. 1970

Coming to the causes of mortality, as shown in Table III.2,
it appears that tuberculosis and fever, either enteric or other
type, take a heavy toll. The grouping of dysentery with
diarrhoea makes it impossible to ascertain their incidence
separately. Therefore, it is difficult to assess the actual incidence of communicable diseases. Incidence of 110 smallpox
cases in the year 1966-67 and 30 in 1967-68 shows a substantial
variation. But the fact remains that it is still very much preva-
lent. These deaths due to infectious and communicable diseases
are surely a reflection on the poor state of public health facilities
in the metropolis.

Birth Rate

Table III.1 also shows that the birth rate of Delhi has registered an upward trend during the years 1962 to 1967, despite
a concentrated drive for family planning, e.g., 29.34 in 1962-
63 and 30.8 in 1967-68. This slight upward trend may as well
be due to better registration system in recent years. However,

even then the birth rate in Delhi is less than that of Bombay (22.8 in 1970) and the all-India average of 40 per thousand.

Health Appraisal

There is an acute paucity of documented information about the health appraisal of Delhi. Besides the studies of Rao and Desai, available information is related to the health appraisal of Central Government Health Scheme beneficiaries. However, mortality study by Dr. Seal (1968-69) on Central Health Service families indicates that during the year 1961 the number of diseases per 100 Government servants was 279 for all the dispensary areas. The survey further revealed that the average attendance of the Government servants in the dispensary was 815. The rate of absence of disease area-wise was recorded to be 24.7 per cent in Kidwai Nagar, 24 per cent in Gole Market, 23.9 per cent in Kasturba Nagar and 9 per cent in Karol Bagh. This shows that area with less density and better health service facilities shows less incidence of mortality.

Rao and Desai, in their survey (1940-57), showed that 50 per cent of the sampled population in Delhi claimed good health, 4.6 per cent had satisfactory health and 8.36 per cent ill health in the previous year. As regards major illness in Delhi, the survey revealed that 5 per cent of diseases accounted for general fever, 10 per cent for stomach troubles, 8 per cent for female diseases and 6 per cent for typhoid and 25 per cent of the cases were of miscellaneous nature.

The areas of high incidence of certain diseases which need immediate public health measures are brought out by the disease pattern during 1956-1963 in a study by Central Government (1963 : 13). It reports as follows :

1. Tilak Nagar area has emerged as an area of maximum incidence of respiratory tuberculosis, whooping cough, anemia, asthma etc.

2. Subzimandi (a congested, low income group) area has been recording maximum incidence of diphtheria for the last six years. It has also recorded highest incidence of (i) diseases of eye other than trachoma, (ii) otitis and mastoiditis, (iii) acute bronchitis, (iv) chronic bronchitis, (v) teeth and gum disease and infection.

3. Karol Bagh has the highest incidence of (i) typhoid, (ii) diabetes and (iii) hypertrophy of tonsils.

4. Minto Road registered maximum incidence of (i) mumps, (ii) trachoma, (iii) influenza, (iv) sore throat and (v) dysentery.

In 1963, the diseases of respiratory system continued to be the largest single group of causes of morbidity and accounted for 27.8 per cent of total sickness during the year.

Hospitalisation

The incidence of hospitalisation among the 61,856 C.G.H.S. beneficiaries, for a period between April to September 1967, was as under :

Maternity cases	2,076
General cases	5,388
Mental cases	9
T.B. cases	232
Cancer cases	2

An idea about the incidence of specific illness among these C.G.H.S. beneficiaries can however be obtained from the reported study of a particular dispensary by Dr. Seal (1968-69), such as :

Abortion	12%
Respiratory	10.3%
Tonsilitis & Sore Throat	8%
Accidents & Injuries	6.9%
Enteric Fever	6.3%
Female Diseases of Ovary & Uterus	5.2%
Heart Disease, Gastro-enteritis	4.01%
Fever	3.4%

An account of hospitalisation of the general population in the major hospitals of Delhi during the year 1967 has been reported as under by the K.N. Rao Committee :

Hospital	Total no. of admissions	
Willingdon	12,082	(General Ward)
	1,525	(Nursing Home)
Safdarjang	50,449	
Hindu Rao	11,700	
Irwin	42,736	
G.B. Pant Hosp.	2,324	
A.I.I.M.S.	9,824	

The above figures would give a partial picture as all hospitals are not included.

Environmental Sanitation

The state of public health services has a great bearing on health status. This has been brought out by Chuttani et al. (1967 : 38-45) in a study of 165 cases admitted in the Infectious Diseases Hospital with reference to their socio-economic status and environmental condition such as housing, water supply and general sanitation, etc. Similar correlationship can be observed from the reported area-wise incidence of cholera in Delhi. Chuttani et al. have observed that greater incidence of cholera was found in the congested northern part of Delhi. Relatively thickly populated South Delhi showed a lower incidence. It was further observed that most of the affected parts were located in the low lying areas of the city and adjacent to the Najafgrah drain. Many of these affected colonies were actually situated adjacent to Municipal dumping grounds. About 96.3 per cent of cholera cases pertained to poor socio-economic groups, e.g., labour class, sweepers and peons. Only 3.7 per cent of the cases were from lower middle class and majority of them were migrants to Delhi. It is worth noting that sewage disposal arrangement did not exist in any of these affected houses. Of 165 households 128 had no latrines and people used open fields and drains for defaecation purposes. Hygienic latrines existed in only 14.9 per cent cases. Thus the study showed a significant relationship between the poor sanitary, sewage condition and the incidence of cholera or gastrointestinal disease. The investigation of source of water supply showed that over 90 per cent cholera cases obtained their drinking water either from open wells or shallow tube-wells. Even those who had had access to municipal tap water, 8.5 per cent were victims of the disease. One hundred and seventeen water samples from different sources were found contaminated in Delhi Municipal Corporation area. The study of food samples proved that food also transmitted infection.

Environmental sanitation was greatly responsible for the health of the pepole. For instance, incidence of tuberculosis is closely related with it. The disease largely being an air borne one, its incidence bears a close relationship to population concentration and environmental sanitation as indicated earlier. The incidence of tuberculosis in Delhi as reported by Gilder Committee (1955) was estimated to be 20,000 while in 1966 this incidence was reported to be 45,000 including 9,000 infectious cases. Thus, it is clear that the environmental sanitation and socio-economic pattern have great bearing on the health status of Delhi population. The present study raises serious questions about the efficiency of the management of the environmental sanitation services in Delhi.

Allied Social Services

Social services play an important part in the health status of the community. Of the social services provided in the city, education, water supply, housing, slum clearance and Urban Community Development are important. As for housing, a study of Town Planning Organisation indicated a relative housing deficit of 1,10,000 dwelling units in 1955-56. In all probability, it may be close to 1,40,000 dwelling units. Besides this deficit, roughly 5 lakhs of people live in deplorable slum conditions and derelict housing. Surveys also indicate that 68.9 per cent of city's population live in one-room dwellings as compared to all-India average of 43.6 per cent. Households living in 2-room dwellings in Delhi form 21.5 per cent as against the all India average of 28.2 per cent. The "privacy index" for Delhi urban area is 3.1 persons per living room. In some areas like Shahdara, the index is 3.6. In some areas about 70 per cent families do not have a bathroom or a lavatory and about 65 per cent have no kitchen (Master Plan of Delhi). These factors have great bearing on the health administration in respect of environmental sanitation and family planning programmes.

The situation in respect of essential services like water supply, sewerage and power supply is nowhere better. The Master Plan (1956) said, "Of the 20 lakhs of urban inhabitants over 3 lakhs do not get protected water supply, about 4 lakhs of people living in new colonies have only intermittent water supply and in many a slum area water scarcity is rather chronic. In the areas of supply, the average per capita water supplied works out to only 40 gallons a day, and this also combines wide disparities." The sewerage system designed about three decades ago for the then population of about 6.5 lakhs is today meeting the needs of 5 times the population. The sewerage system serves only parts of Old Delhi and New Delhi areas with some of their extensions to the south and to the west. In Old Delhi, the walled city of Shahjahanabad, perhaps not more than 20 per cent of the dwellings are connected to the sewerage system and are without flush latrines. The areas having no sewerage system lie in all directions of the central core of the city. The entire Cantonment area (about 10,000 acres) and Shahdara (about 25,000 acres) have no sewerage system. The situation, though since improved, still leaves a serious hangover. In the absence of authoritative information, it is not possible to indicate the improvements.

Provision of Health Services

We have so far studied the health status of Delhi. But in order to comprehend the problem in all its dimensions it will be appropriate to proceed to enumerate the health services provided by various agencies in Delhi. Although the study is mainly of the municipal government, it is also necessary to understand other agencies engaged in providing health services in the metropolis.

The health services of Delhi are provided mainly by three agencies, viz., municipal, non-municipal and private medical bodies.

Municipal Services

a—Maternity and Child Care Services
b—School Health Scheme
c—Immunization Centre
d—Cleansing and Scavenging
e—Medical Care (General & Specialised)
f—Water Supply and Sewage Disposal

All these services are provided by the Delhi Municipal Corporation, New Delhi Municipal Committee, and the Cantonment Board in their respective jurisdictions. The services regarding the Delhi Municipal Corporation will be discussed in subsequent chapters in greater detail. Water supply and sewage disposal are undertaken by a Special Committee of the Corporation for the whole of Delhi. This matter is beyond the scope of the present study and we shall restrict only to other governmental, medical and public health services.

Medical Care

Medical care refers to the provision of hospitals and dispensaries for restoration of health. Medical care of general nature and specialised services and the maternity home service are provided by the Central Government and the Delhi Administration, besides the Municipal Corporation.

In addition to maternity homes, some other specialised services are also provided by private and autonomous bodies. Factories in Delhi have health services as a part of their welfare service under the Factories Act. Voluntary organisations and autonomous bodies also provide health services for Delhi.

It is clear that while the bulk of the public health provisions are taken care of by the municipality, the medical care is shared by all the three groups of agencies. A detailed examination of the medical care may, therefore, be relevant at this stage.

. Before discussing the medical services in Delhi Union Territory we may give as a background the position of hospitals in India. Jain Committee (1968) on the position of hospitals remarks that of the 4,000 hospitals in India, 160 are teaching hospitals, 1,219 are at District Headquarters and 2,053 at Tehsil Headquarters. Of the 335 districts in this country, 37% have hospitals with more than 100 beds; 27 per cent have hospitals having 100 to 200 beds. About 36 per cent of these beds are in rural areas and the rest in urban areas. Out of the 5,200 blocks in this country, 4,973 have one Primary Health Centre each with about 6 beds in each of them serving a population from 60,000 to 1,00,000, although the Bhore Committee had recommended one unit for about 40,000 population. The Primary Health Centres constitute 11 per cent of the total bed strength. On this basis the bed-population ratio in rural area is one bed for 3,700 persons and for urban area it works out to 1,520. But looking at the availability of hospital facilities from the point of view of service to community, the studies show that hospital and dispensary services are catering to only 15 per cent of the sickness of the community. The rest are headed by private physicians or other forms of medical care. The total number of beds in all hospitals in this country works out in a ratio of 0.6 per 1,000. Of these hospitals, 81 per cent are maintained by the Government and 19 per cent by private organisations.

The Hospital Review Committees on Delhi hospitals (1962) and (1968) report that about Rs. 7,000 per bed per annum are spent on 8,000 hospital beds in the metropolis. The ratio of bed per population in Delhi is 2.2 per one thousand population against the national average of 0.6. But assuming that 36 per cent of the total beds are rural beds, the average bed-population ratio in urban area in India comes down to 1 : 520. Delhi is privileged to have 20 : 1000 ratio against the national average of 10 : 1000 (Krishnaswamy Rao 1970). Numerically, Delhi can claim the largest assemblage of hospitals, nursing homes and welfare centres in India.

With the influx of population and the increasing import- ance of Delhi, the number of hospitals and dispensaries increased from 14 in 1949 to 27 in 1956 and from 24 to 69 respectively. The new unit of "health centre" also emerged to 15 from 10 in 1969 (see Appendix A.2 for the list of hospitals). As indicated earlier, the medical care of Delhi is shared by various agencies other than the Municipal Corporation, such as

New Delhi Municipal Committee, Railways, Employees' State Insurance, Central Government Health Scheme and Delhi Administration and private agencies. Of the organisations of medical care (personal health), the Municipal Corporation has about 25 per cent of the total beds located in eight institutions. It will be discussed in detail in the subsequent chapter. The medical care of Delhi is shared by the following agencies.

Railways

Railways have a Central Hospital in the Connaught Circus area for the exclusive use of Railway employees and their families with 250 beds.

Employees' State Insurance Scheme

The scheme provides for medical care arrangement through a network of dispensaries for the insured industrial workers and their families. It is building its own hospital of 924 beds, in north-west of Delhi.

Central Government Health Service

The C.G.H.S. Scheme seeks to provide comprehensive medical services for all government servants and their families in Delhi. The service includes promotional, preventive and curative, e.g., outdoor treatment, supply of necessary drugs, laboratory and X-ray treatment, investigation, domiciliary visit, ambulance service, inpatient service treatment, specialist care, confinement, ante-natal, post-natal, women and baby clinic, emergency treatment, supply of optical and dental aids at scheduled rates, advice on family planning, including supply of free contraceptive appliances, health check-up and immunisation and preventive medicine. It was started in 1954 in Delhi, and was later on extended to Bombay. It aims to give medical aid and charge contributions according to the means of the wage earners from Re. 0.50 to Rs. 12 per month. The C.G.H.S. Scheme aims to ensure the continuity of the care at the home, clinic and hospital. There are now 61 dispensaries of which three are mobile, three Ayurvedic and two Homoeopathic. The scheme covers about 6,00,000 people and average attendance at the dispensaries per day is 25,000. The number of doctors is 400, and 33 dispensaries are visited by medical specialist and 12 by skin specialist. There are 16 regional laboratories, 10 paediatric centres for immunization against smallpox, polio and other diseases.

The Central Government Health Service Scheme has established a well-knit clinic and domiciliary service. It is supported by the specialist services at the hospital out-patients, poly-clinics and at the home of the patient where required. The Safdarjang Hospital, Willingdon Hospital and Lady Hardinge Hospital, Victoria Zanana and Holy Family Hospitals are utilised for institutional maternity cases.

Ministry of Defence

Military Hospital and nine general hospitals located in Cantonment area provide medical care to Defence personnel and their families.

Delhi Administration

Health being a state subject, the hospitals like Irwin, Police, Maulana Azad, Pandit Pant, Shahdara and Poor House are the institutions directly managed by the Delhi Administration, since 1958.

Autonomous Bodies

Lady Hardinge, All India Institute of Medical Sciences, Kalavati Saran Children Hospital, Lady Hardinge Medical College, Ram Saroop T.B. Hospital, all have autonomous governing bodies for administration with Director General of Health Services as Chairman, except All India Institute of Medical Sciences, which is primarily an educational and research institute.

The Hospital Review Committee (1969) commends the useful service done by six Sevika Centres working in Karol Bagh, Subzi Mandi and providing medical and preventive care to lower middle class.

Voluntary Organisations and Private Trusts

St. Stephen's Hospital (Tis Hazari), Holy Family Hospital (Okhla), Shroff's Eye Hospital (Daryaganj), Sant Parmanand Eye Hospital (Civil Lines), Model Eye Hospital (Lajpat Nagar), Jaisa Ram Hospital (Karol Bagh), Delhi Maternity Hospital (Pusa Road), Tirath Ram Hospital and Nursing Home (Civil Lines) with 110 beds, are the main institutional medical services in Delhi. There are also additional 300 beds run by private nursing homes governed by Nursing Home Act, 1956 (see Appendix A.2).

All the findings above suggest that till 1957, Delhi Administration used to provide the maximum services, through provision of more than 50 per cent of the beds in the metropolis. The aggregate number of beds in Greater Delhi rose by 2,760 or 164 per cent from 1,629 in 1947 to 4,389 in 1957 which is in keeping with the general trend obtaining in the country. In the course of 1941-61, population of Delhi has gone up from 7 lakhs to 2.4 million leading to creation of more hospitals which are managed by various authorities.

In the following chapter we shall deal with the administrative framework within which the Health Department plans and administers its services.

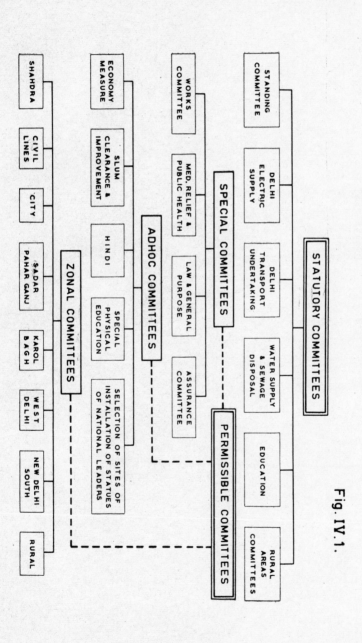

Committees Under Municipal Corporation Of Delhi

Fig. IV.1.

STATUTORY COMMITTEES

- STANDING COMMITTEE
- DELHI ELECTRIC SUPPLY
- DELHI TRANSPORT UNDERTAKING
- WATER SUPPLY & SEWAGE DISPOSAL
- EDUCATION
- RURAL AREAS COMMITTEES

SPECIAL COMMITTEES

- WORKS COMMITTEE
- MED. RELIEF & PUBLIC HEALTH
- LAW & GENERAL PURPOSE
- ASSURANCE COMMITTEE

ADHOC COMMITTEES

- ECONOMY MEASURE
- SLUM CLEARANCE & IMPROVEMENT
- HINDI
- SPECIAL PHYSICAL EDUCATION

PERMISSIBLE COMMITTEES

- SELECTION OF SITES OF INSTALLATION OF STATUES OF NATIONAL LEADERS

ZONAL COMMITTEES

- SHAHDRA
- CIVIL LINES
- CITY
- SADAR PAHAR GANJ
- KAROL BAGH
- WEST DELHI
- NEW DELHI SOUTH
- RURAL

CHAPTER IV

Health Department : Institutional Framework

Social services in a town are organised within the institutional framework of a local body, which has a statutory existence. In order, therefore, to understand the organisation of these services it is essential to briefly enumerate the set up of the Corporation and its various departments.

We have already mentioned in Chapter II that the Corporation funtions through its deliberative (Committee system) and executive (Commissioner) wings. Figure IV.1 illustrates the different types of Committees with their names which are functioning at the Corporation level.

Standing Committee

Of all the Committees, the Standing Committee is the decision-making body of the Corporation. Standing Committee along with the Commissioner and the other Statutory Committees and the Council is responsible for the efficient performance of Corporation functions. The Standing Committee consists of fourteen members, who are elected by the Councillors and Aldermen from among themselves.

All matters falling within the purview of a Committee are routed to the Corporation through the Standing Committee. An urgent matter may directly be placed before the Council or the Standing Committee.

65

The Standing Committee exercises such powers and performs such functions as are specifically conferred or imposed on it by and under the Act. The Standing Committee is authorised to deal with all financial matters up to a limit of Rs. 15,000/- and any other cases delegated to it by the Corporation. In case of contract, the Standing Committee is empowered to decide cases upto any amount above Rs. 10,000/-. But the estimate has to be sanctioned both by the Standing Committee and the Corporation. The budget has to go through the Standing Committee before its submission to the Corporation. Creation of all posts with a salary of less than Rs. 350/- per month and the creation of temporary posts for six months with a minimum monthly salary of Rs. 250/- or more are within the powers of the Standing Committee.

As regards the procedures for the meetings, the Delhi Municipal Corporation (Procedure and Conduct of Business) Regulations, 1958, are strictly observed. The Standing Committee meetings are normally held once a week. If the Committee omits to fix the date, time and place of the meeting, it is fixed by the Chairman of the respective Committee. The chairman of a committee, whenever he thinks fit, on a written requisition signed by the Commissioner or by more than three members of the committee can immediately call a special meeting of the committee for the transaction of any important business. The official records indicate that the Standing Committee, as a rule, does not meet once in a week. But in practice, during the budget session it meets daily for consecutive 6 or 7 days a week. Study of the records indicates the number of meetings held during the last four years, as given below :

Year	No. of meetings held
1965-66	82
1966-67	48
1967-68	70
1968-69	69

The figures above reveal that by and large the Standing Committee met more than once in a week during the last four

ORGANIZATION OF MEDICAL AND PUBLIC HEALTH DEPARTMENT
DELHI MUNICIPAL CORPORATION AS ON JULY 1969

Fig IV. 2.

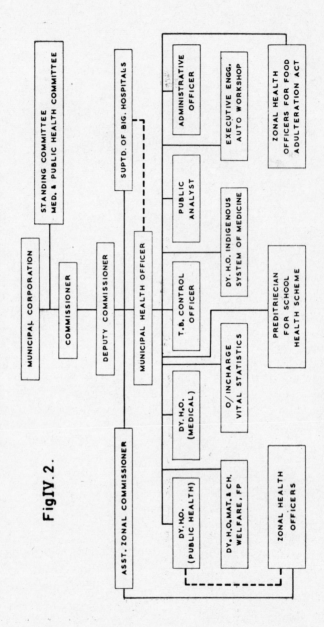

Indirect Control ----- Direct Control ——

years. The drop in the number in 1966-67 to 48 was attributed to Councillors' preoccupation with the election campaign. An analysis of the minutes of the Standing Committee revealed that the cases discussed in the Standing Committee related, for example, to financial sanction, creation of posts, sanction of leave or disciplinary action against some officials. The organisation and establishment seem to occupy a prominent place in the discussions.

Special Zonal Committees

Zonal Committee is one of the special committees of the Corporation. Under Section 40 of the D.M.C. Act 1957, each zone has a special zonal committee consisting of the Councillors from the wards within its jurisdiction and one or more Aldermen as determined by the Corporation, like the Borough Committee in Calcutta. The powers and functions of the Zonal Committees can be classified into matters relating to "consideration" of proposals, making of recommendations, review of work progress and inquiry and advice. The most important power delegated to the Zonal Committee is the sanction of estimates and plans for works to be carried out in the zones (other than those relating to any of the Undertakings) upto Rs. 25,000/-, provided that provision exists in the budget sanctioned by the Corporation. Since the decentralisation of Corporation in 1965, all zonal matters are discussed at the Zonal Committee prior to its placement before the Corporation Council. Formal organisation of the Municipal Corporation is given in Fig. IV. 2.

Medical Relief and Public Health Committee

The Medical Relief and Public Health Committee is one of the special committees set up in 1958 to deal with matters concerning medical relief, public health and sanitation of the metropolis. This committee consists of 15 members as per D.M.C. (Procedure and Conduct of Business) Regulations, 1958.

As a special committee, the Medical Relief and Public Health Committee is a non-statutory advisory body without any financial or appointing authority. The Medical Relief and Public Health Committee is scheduled to meet once in a fortnight, on alternate Wednesdays. The number of meetings held during the last four years is as follows :

Year	No. of meetings held
1965-66	29
1966-67	18
1967-68	23
1968-69	21

The figures above show that on an average the Committee held meetings once a fortnight during 1965-1969. The drop in the number of meetings held in 1966-67 could be attributed to the members' preoccupation with elections in that year. It is therefore evident that they meet quite regularly.

An analysis of the composition of the Health Committee reveals that the members of the Health Committee are not selected because of their knowledge or interest in public health or medical matters. However, the records show that during 1969-70 and 1970-71 a Vaid was elected as Chairman of the Health Committee. Dr. Bhim Sen Bansal and Dr. Radheylal Aggarwal were two Ayurvedic doctors elected to the Health Committee in 1969-70, whereas there were seven more doctors as Councillors of the Corporation. The Health Committee is a big body of 15 people drawn from different areas and professions. Normally the decision of the Committee has to be forwarded to the Corporation for its ratification.

Minutes of the meeting of the Health Committee held on 16 July, 1969, at Town Hall reveal that out of ten cases on the agenda, discussion on one case was postponed, five cases were only recorded, one case was preferred to the Commissioner for report. There were suggestions for opening of Animal Husbandry Section at Kotla Mubarakpur and further extension of new licences to be issued to particular vendors. There have been instances where the Health Committee made special recommendations for prevention of epidemic diseases. But the cross-check with the Standing Committee meetings revealed that the decision-making authority did not take any action on such recommendations. It is therefore evident that the Health Committee is purely an advisory body. It is not mandatory to ratify its recommendations.

Organisation of Health Services

The Health Services of the Corporation derive its legal sanction from Sections 41, 42 and 43 of the 1957 Act as amended upto 1961 and the rules, regulations and the bye-laws made thereunder. Section 42 of the 1957 Act, as modified upto 1961, provides for public health, scavenging and medical care as some of the obligatory duties of the Corporation. Chapter XVII further enumerates the service provisions in regard to sanitation and public health. Besides, the Infectious Diseases Act, Food Adulteration Act and the All India Health Act passed early in this century provide legal support to the Health Department.

The local body has two-fold responsibilities—obligatory and discretionary. Of the obligatory functions vested in the Municipal Corporation, the following are concerned with public health and medical activities:

(a) Construction, maintenance and cleansing of drains and drainage works and of public latrines, urinals and similar conveniences (construction of drains is Public Health Engineering Department's job; Sewage Disposal Department is also responsible for some of these activities).

(b) Regulation of places for disposal of the dead and the provision and maintenance of places for the said purposes.

(c) Registration of births and deaths.

(d) Public vaccination and inoculation.

(e) Measures for prevention and checking of the spread of dangerous diseases.

(f) Establishment and maintenance of hospitals, dispensaries and maternity and child welfare centres and carrying out the measures necessary for public medical relief.

(g) Watering and cleansing of public streets and other places.

Of the discretionary functions entrusted to the Corporation the following are concerned with public health and medical relief activities:

(a) Establishment and maintenance of veterinary hospitals.

(b) Organisation or management of chemical or bacteriological laboratories for the analysis of water, food and drugs for the detection of diseases or research connected with public health or medical relief.

(c) Organisation, construction, maintenance and management of swimming pools, public wash-houses, bathing places and other institutions designed for improvement of public health.

(d) Any measure not hereinbefore specifically mentioned but likely to promote public safety, health convenience or general welfare.

Formal Organisation

The formal organisation of the health department has been changing with the changes in the administrative set up of the local authority. There are certain functions which are within the jurisdiction of the Municipal Corporation, whereas the others are the responsibility of the Delhi Administration and the Central Government. Figure IV.3 gives the formal organisation of health services under the sphere of the Delhi Administration.

Delhi Administration

Furthermore, the Acts of 1935 and 1951 made the State responsible for health services. Considering the character of Delhi, its structural set up was differently designed. The Superintendent of Medical Services is in overall charge of health services in Delhi. There is also an examining body for Ayurvedic and Unani Systems of Medicine presided over by the Superintendent of Medical Services. A Family Planning Centre and a Hospital for Mental Diseases in Shahdara, besides the Irwin Hospital and Maulana Abul Kalam Azad Medical College, are under the direct control of the Superintendent of Medical Services, Delhi.

ORGANIZATION OF HEALTH DEPARTMENT OF DELHI ADMINISTRATION

Medical Services And Family Planning Directorate

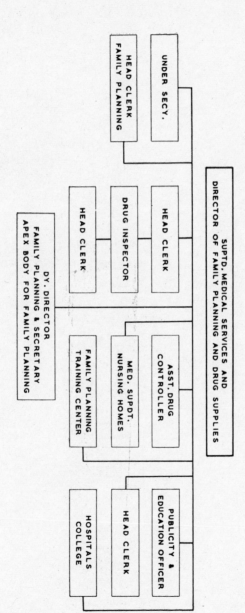

Fig. IV. 3

Inter-governmental Relations

The relations between the Central department and the local authorities are governed by legislation. According to Delhi Administration Act 1966, all powers regarding the administration of services in Delhi Union Territory are vested in the Central Government. Except the right of supersession, all other powers of the Central Government are delegated to the Lt. Governor. Thus the Chief Executive Councillor of the Delhi Administration exercises only advisory control over the local government. However, the Central Government has powers of inspection and right to issue regulations and the local authority has to submit its proposals to the Central Government for ministerial approval.

Municipal Health Officer

Section 89 of the 1957 Act provides for the appointment of the Municipal Health Officer as the functional head of the Health Department of the Corporation. Section 394 of the Act provides for the Municipal Health Officer to function as the Chief Registrar of Births and Deaths in Delhi and to be responsible for vital statistics. He is also the Food Hygiene Authority and the Inspector of Slaughter Houses for Delhi. Thus the Municipal Health Officer is delegated with all health executive functions of the Health Department as enumerated by the Act, except the supervision of two big Corporation hospitals, which are directly controlled by the Deputy Commissioner.

The Municipal Health Officer, in his general supervision work, is assisted by the Deputy Health Officers, in charge of six functional sections, viz., Public Health, Medical Care, Maternity and Child Welfare, Indigenous Medicine, Malaria Control and T.B. Eradication Programme. Furthermore, he is assisted by the Statistical Officer and Workshop Engineer, Public Analyst, Administrative Officer (Health) and Zonal Health Officer (headquarters). Recently the posts of Deputy Directors, Malaria and T.B. and Smallpox have been combined. The first line supervisors in the zone are the Zonal Health Officers for eight zones. Besides the headquarters officials, about 2,500 technical field staff consisting of 346 doctors, 107 public health nurses, 285 nursing staff, 48 dentists, 148 laboratory assistants, 70 laboratory technicians, one medical social worker, 110 dressers among others are employed in the Health Department.

The School Medical Scheme financially under the control of the Education Department is run by a Paediatrician, directly under the Municipal Health Officer. The Zonal Health Officer is the supervisor at the zonal level for the School Health Programme. A full team of 16 doctors and 17 public health nurses are at present working under this scheme.

The Health Department is classified under four distinct groups, *viz.*, (i) Public Health and Environmental Sanitation, (ii) Prevention of Communicable Diseases, (iii) Maternity and Child Welfare and Family Planning, and (iv) Medical Care Services.

DIVISION OF FUNCTIONS

Deputy Health Officer (Public Health)

The Deputy Health Officer for Public Health is assigned duties like conservancy services, prevention and control of communicable diseases, vaccination, bureau of epidemiology, prevention of food adulteration and food sampling work, health education and publicity, inspection, regulation, control and licensing of food shops and certain other trades as provided in Public Health Bye-laws, public crematorium, inspection of slaughter houses etc. In the hundred constituencies of Delhi one Sanitary Inspector is empowered to act as Food Inspector under this Section.

During the period of study, the Deputy Director in charge of T.B. Control was also made in charge of Malaria Control and Smallpox Eradication Programme for Delhi. Of late, he has been given charge of communicable diseases section also.

Deputy Health Officer (Maternity & Child Welfare)

The Deputy Health Officer (M.C.H.) is in overall charge of the Section. She is primarily responsible for Maternity &

Child Welfare Centres, Foundling Homes for Abandoned Boys and Girls, Maternity Homes, Maternity Hospitals, Family Planning Centres, Nutrition, School Medical Schemes and Training of Dais. A Special District Officer for Family Planning is in overall charge of Family Planning Programme (see Chapter VI for details).

Deputy Health Officer (Medical)

Deputy Health Officer (Medical) is entrusted with duties like administration of the Corporation hospitals and dispensaries, control of Primary Health Centres (rural and urban), control of specialist clinics, *viz.*, V.D., Leprosy, Dental, T.B. etc. (at present the T.B. Control Officer is in charge of all T.B. Clinics in Delhi). His job also includes controlling of State health laboratory, purchase and supply of medical stores and equipments for medical institutions, execution of the planned schemes and management of training schools for nurses.

Public Analyst

A scientist in charge of Public Analyst Section of the Laboratory is responsible for analysis of food samples in the food laboratory, prosecution files in food cases, compilation of reports and returns on the subject of food adulteration and its control, technical matters relating to the implementation of Prevention of Food Adulteration Act 1954 and Prevention of Food Adulteration Rules, 1955, initiation of proposals with regard to food standards and pursuing them with the Central Committee for Food Standards.

Statistical Officer (Health)

A full-fledged Statistical Unit with the 56 registration centres established with Central Government grants-in-aid is under the control of the Statistical Officer (Health).

Zonal Health Officer (Headquarters)

He assists the Municipal Health Officer in pursuing the progress of the Plan schemes, loan works and other new proposals. He works in liaison with Deputy Health Officer, Municipal Engineer, Drainage Engineer, Architect and other agencies to expedite the planned schemes. He also looks after food adulteration with the help of a Central Food Squad consisting of 8 Inspectors. He is in charge of maintenance of Sanitary Stores.

Administrative Officer (Health)

He is responsible for all administrative and establishment affairs of the Health Department. The study reveals that an Assistant promoted to the post of Administrative Officer is at present dealing with all the administrative affairs of technical officers and the department.

Zonal Health Officer

Zonal Health Officer is responsible for all public health and medical care activities at the zonal level. His duties can be classified under two heads :

(a) *Public Health*

1. Prevention of communicable diseases.
2. Maternity and child care and family planning through Corporation Centres.
3. Health education programme in the area through Corporation and other schools :
   (a) environmental sanitation,
   (b) facilities for pure drinking water,
   (c) education of teachers and children in health habits,
   (d) applied nutrition programme.
4. Compilation of vital statistics.
5. Community Project Health Programme of the area, e.g., dug well latrine, smokeless oven, dry type of latrine to be converted to flush latrine, to provide sewer line.

(b) Environmental Sanitation

1. Prevention of food adulteration under the Prevention of Food Adulteration Act 1954 and Epidemics Act.
2. Legal action against public traders for violation of Municipal Act and bye-laws, e.g., creation of nuisance, insanitation, running of different food establishments without securing valid sanction as laid down in the particular Act/Bye-law of the Municipal Corporation, Delhi, destruction of unwholesome food.
3. Control of rabies by destruction of stray dogs through Sanitary Inspectors.
4. Disinfection of wells.

Structural Problems

Administrative organisation is designed to achieve the set goals. This requires unity of command with scope for horizontal and vertical coordination. The roles should be arranged in such a manner that it allows for flow of communication at various levels. These important organisational elements seemed to be missing in the health department under discussion. Duties were distributed on the basis of the job specialisation and not on territorial basis. This resulted in two problems. Firstly, there was no inter- and intra-departmental coordination. Secondly the administration was virtually in the hands of the lay political amateurs. The Municipal Secretary can hardly find time for important decisions. Under the circumstances, it is natural that the staff would be more prone to political and other pressures. Thus pressure groups have more influence on decision-making, regardless of the rational justification of the case. This leads to strained relationship between the executive authorities and the Council. Having little time at their disposal to concentrate on matters, the Standing Committee members would be more prone to oblige the executives rallying round them. It was, therefore, revealed that the Health Officers and other officers with independent views were mostly in conflict with the Council. Small advisory committees consisting of eminent public men in the respective fields and experts on the subject for each unit of the department can be a solution to the problem.

Thirdly the organisational structure leads to dual control over staff at the zonal level. The field specialists at the zonal level, like hospital doctors, family planning doctors, malaria control officer, smallpox officer were both responsible to the Zonal Health Officer as well as to their parent department in the Corporation. This dual control over the officers at the zonal level tended to create hostile relationship between the Zonal Health Officer and the line workers in the field, leading to tension and rivalry. It became difficult for Zonal Health Officer also to control the officers under his jurisdiction due to this dual control.

Thus the organisational structure of the Corporation Health Department as the study shows has great scope for improvement and further development.

Activity Analysis Of The Health Department
Delhi Municipal Corporation

Fig. V. 1

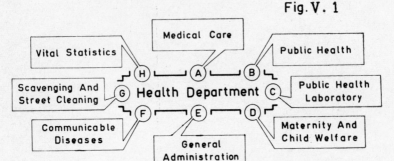

A Medical Care

HOSPITALS
COLONY HOSPITALS
SPECIALISED HOSPITALS
AYURVEDIC HOSPITALS
X-RAY FACILITIES
FREE BLOOD TRANSFUSION
LEPROSY CLINICS
URBAN HEALTH CENTRE
V.D. CLINICS
RURAL HEALTH CENTRE
MEDICAL STORES

B Public Health

FREE AMBULANCE FOR
INFECTIOUS DISEASES
CREMATION GROUND
FUNERAL VAN
DISPOSAL OF DEAD ANIMALS
VACCINATION
RODENT CONTROL
FOOD ADULTERATION CONTROL
STREET CLEANING
CHOLERA CONTROL
MAINTENANCE OF WORKSHOP & VANS

C Public Health Laboratory

CENTRAL LABORATORIES
SANITATION ANALYSIS
WATER SAMPLING
FOOD ANALYSIS

D Maternity And Child Welfare

MATERNITY HOMES
HEALTH EDUCATION
SCHOOL MEDICAL SCHEME
FAMILY PLANNING CENTRE
FAMILY PLANNING SUB CENTRE

E General Administration

BUDGET
SUPPLIES AND STORES
MAINTENANCE
BUSINESS MANAGEMENT

F Communicable Diseases

ANTI MALARIA OPERATION
SMALLPOX ERADICATION
T.B. CONTROL
IMMUNISATION CENTRES

G Scavenging And Street Cleaning

H Vital Statistics

REGISTRATION OF BIRTH AND
CONTROL
HEALTH RECORDS

CHAPTER V

Health Department : Activity Analysis

The activity and services of a department are the product of an effort at translating its objectives into action in a given organisational structure. The translation of a purpose into programme of services involves a series of steps in administration.

It is axiomatic in all broad programmes of the community services that the resources are never sufficient to undertake a wide variety of programmes to meet the needs of all sections of the community. Thus, it becomes essential to have, what may seem as "priorities in programme planning". The establishment of priority is a major responsibility of the Health Officer.

Analysis of the activities of the Health Department as seen in the appended Fig. V.1 shows that they are varied and interrelated. These functions can be broadly classified into welfare, supervisory, regulative and promotional.

The activities have grown and expanded in response to the needs of the community, for instance, some of the services recently undertaken by the department are : maternity and child health, health education, family planning, school health programme, medical care, health statistics. The laboratory activities and polio vaccination have recently been added. In

77

addition the control of Tuberculosis, V.D. and Leprosy work are carried on through specialised clinics. Electric crematorium is a recent addition to the public health activities. Epidemiology section, which was created in 1968, was closed down in 1970 due to financial stringency.

As indices of the growth of the local health department, three criteria on which information is available are: (i) the extent of geographic area covered by the local health department, (ii) annual expenditure of the local health department, and (iii) the number of full-time local public health personnel with their speciality. The personnel and expenditure pattern of the department during the last five years indicates the expansion of services.

In the following pages, an attempt has been made to study the activities of some of the units of the department. Issues involved in the management of activities as examined in the chapter are : (i) nature and substance of the services, (ii) availability of services, (iii) mode of rendering services and problems, and (iv) public acceptance in case of medical care services.

The Corporation has made two divisions of its activities for administrative purposes, i.e., (i) Public Health (environmental sanitation) and (ii) Medical Relief (curative services).

Public Health

Under the first one, the most important is conservancy and scavenging. The main object of the conservancy and scavenging programme is complete sewering of urbanized area, roads and the households. Corporation is authorised to get the premises cleaned and to pursue the construction of authorised drains and urinals for sanitation purposes. The section has established standard methods for the construction of septic tank and provision of sewer latrine in case of dry latrine.

The rapid population growth and resultant increase in new residential areas, authorised or unauthorised, require adequate provision of latrines and urinals and safe disposal of sewage and other wastes. In highly dense areas special arrangements are being made to dispose of night soil and garbage, besides the night soil of the stray animals moving around the roads.

It has all along been obligatory on the part of local authorities to provide a sufficient number of public urinals and latrines and to keep private and public premises clean and sanitary. In regard to the latter function the executive authority is endowed with power to regulate sanitary conditions of private premises in sanctioning the building plans as per health bye-law no. 3. Corporation might notify any trade mentioned in the list as dangerous and offensive and prohibit any one from carrying it on without licence. Any person desiring to enter any trade in the notified area should apply to the executive authority at least thirty days before the commencement of the year.

The Corporation engages about 8,236 permanent, 2,522 part-time and another 2,000 sweepers of different categories to clean its 5,987 kilometre roads. About 10% of the aforesaid roads is kutcha. Besides, the Corporation along with New Delhi Municipal Committee is also responsible to clean 170 kms of roads maintained by the Central Public Works Department. The newly constructed Jhuggi-Jhopri areas are mostly without public latrines. The roads close to these unauthorised residential areas are also cleaned by the Corporation.

Sweepers engaged in cleanliness operations with brooms and 1,000 wheel boroughs collect dust and garbage from roads and the wayside drains and deposit them in 350 dust-bins and 90 dalos scattered all over the city. The licensed sweepers also clean private residential premises and dump the rubbish in the dust-bins. They also clean the drains adjacent to the residential areas. They also clean the dust-bins once a week and dump the garbage at a particular place.

The Corporation is also required to clean the night soil from the kutcha dry latrines in the residential premises in Chandni Chowk, Bara Hindu Rao and Kingsway area. About 40% of the total latrines in City Zone are of dry type. In some of the highly congested areas, where the truck cannot enter, the 'pail schdutes' are deployed to dispose of the night soil with the help of big cranes.

Public Health activities are performed by the eight Zonal Health Officers, responsible for their respective zones. In each

Zone the Health Officer is assisted by the Chief Sanitary
Inspector. Large areas like Karol Bagh and City
Zone have two Chief Sanitary Inspectors each. Chief Sanitary
Inspectors are assisted by the Sanitary Inspectors, whose
number varies with the number of constituencies in the zone.
The Corporation engages six more Sanitary Inspectors for
each zone for refuse removal operations. Three Sewer Gang
Inspectors are engaged for sewage disposal under these Sanitary Inspectors for refuse removal. The sweepers are supervised by the "beldars" or "gang leaders". An Executive
Engineer is in charge of the Workshop to maintain the vehicles, used for the refuse removal operations in each zone
(see Fig. V.2). It may be worth mentioning here that there is
no provision for Sanitary Inspectors in Rural Area Zone.

The study team on "Collection and Disposal of Refuse"
of the Committee on Plan Projects (Building Projects Team),
states that the cardinal principles of the Refuse Disposal
Operations are (a) efficiency and cost must be kept in proper
perspective, (b) use of modern techniques, properly trained
and qualified persons, and (c) business-like handling of needs
by maintaining strict and accurate costing return for each
phase of operation.

Refuse removal operations need trucks for carrying dirt
from the dust-bins and dispose them of in a dumping area.
The officials interviewed pointed out that of the 146 trucks
needed by the Unit, only 86 were in satisfactory condition.
The job of refuse disposal is given to the South Zone on
contract basis. The maintenance and repair of trucks are
managed by the Workshop Engineer attached to the Health
Department. Of the available trucks attached to Public Health
Unit, the official records suggest that 47 trucks are second
rate and 19 third rate. It was found that even the first-class
trucks were making three trips a day. Thus for cleaning
garbage the problem is not merely of availability of trucks
but also of proper utilization of the existing fleet of trucks.

Another problem is of finding dumping sites. The sites
close to residential areas are also used although at the peril
of public health. This is being resisted by the people of the
area as indicated by some of the officials. But the authorities

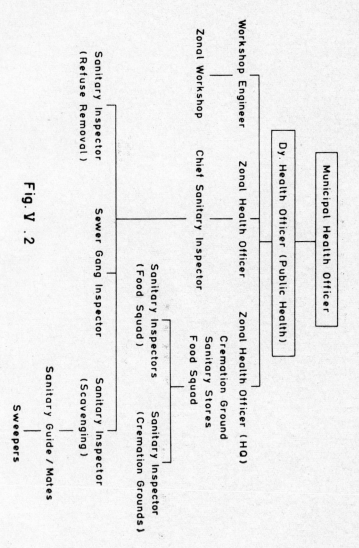

Organisation In Public Health Division

Municipal Health Officer

Dy. Health Officer (Public Health)

Workshop Engineer — Zonal Health Officer — Zonal Health Officer (HQ)

Zonal Workshop — Chief Sanitary Inspector

Cremation Ground
Sanitary Stores
Food Squad

Sanitary Inspector
(Refuse Removal)

Sewer Gang Inspector

Sanitary Inspectors
(Food Squad)

Sanitary Inspector
(Scavenging)

Sanitary Inspector
(Cremation Grounds)

Sanitary Guide / Mates

Sweepers

Fig. V . 2

are facing a serious problem of finding suitable dumping grounds for garbage.

Besides, distribution of trucks and the sweepers to different zones does not seem to be done on any rational basis leading to problems of effective utilization of existing resources. It is well demonstrated by inequitable distribution of trucks and sweepers for different areas of the city.

TABLE V.1

Deployment of Sweepers and Trucks in relation to Population

Zone	Population figures*	Sweepers†	Trucks‡
City	7,15,564	1,992	42
Sadar Paharganj		1,234	25
Karol Bagh	3,23,311	2,048	24
Civil Lines, Subzimandi	3,62,176	1,512	24
South Delhi	1,15,577	2,400	10
Shahdara	1,50,674	1,438	15
West Delhi	1,71,596	1,538	11
Transferred Area	2,22,860	—	—

* Census of India, 1961, Vol. XIX, Pt. II
† & ‡ are compiled from the sectional reports

The table above clearly points to the disparity in deployment of sweepers and trucks in different areas of Delhi. For instance, West Delhi and Shahdara although more densely populated than South Delhi, had less number of sweepers and less of trucks. The population had undergone major changes during the last twelve years in different zones, with no proportional change either in the staff or in the number of trucks.

The Organisation and Methods Division, in their report, estimated that the total requirement of the Corporation would be 157 drivers and 628 sweepers including the reserve of 30% of the total strength. It is further brought out that the vehicles, the sweepers and their supervisors are not allotted to various zones on the basis of actual need as determined by their workload and on accepted yardstick of performance as decided by the O&M Division. The dumping sites were generally not allocated to the refuse removal vehicles, keeping in view the proximity of the area to the dumping site. This results in extra mileage and wasteful expenditure.

The Corporation is also to provide sanitary services to the newly built Delhi Development Authority colonies on prescribed payment. But usually the Delhi Development Authority is not in a position to pay this amount to the Corporation, as they take time to recover the amount from the residents. This results in crisis in the environmental sanitation. This problem is said to be further aggravated by the dual control over sweepers working in the newly built colonies. The health officials pointed out that sweepers drawing salary from Delhi Development Authority Head Office resist the control of the Corporation. This dual loyalty results in poor sanitary conditions in some of the newly built D.D.A. colonies, which are inhabited largely by lower middle class people.

A visit to some of these colonies, which are offshoots of the Jhuggi-Jhopri Removal Scheme of the Corporation, reveals that there is no proper arrangement for garbage collection. Most people throw their refuse at a convenient place along the road and leave it for the authorities to clear. The garbage collection truck is supposed to come once a week, but the local people pointed out that it hardly appeared once in two or three weeks.

It was further pointed out by the O&M Division of the Corporation that the refuse removal vehicles and staff of Karol Bagh, Sadar Paharganj and City, at present based at the Jhandewalan workshop, were proving rather uneconomic. Actually, they should have been shifted to the existing City North Zone which could be strengthened with better workshop facilities. This inter-zone depot at the City North Depot could operate as a single administrative unit. The refuse removal operations should be under the Zonal Chief Sanitary Inspector, except for the City North Zone which should have one whole-time Sanitary Inspector, directly under the Deputy Health Officer (Public Health).

In order to improve attendance in conservancy work, strict discipline needs to be enforced in regard to the drivers and lorry labour. Urgent action is warranted for proper utilisation of surplus vehicles and staff engaged in the refuse removal set up. The O&M Division stated that streamlining of the organisation and deployment of sweepers and trucks could result in a saving of Rs. 5 lakhs per year in Corporation budget.

Sanitary Staff Requirement

The O&M Division calculated that out of 330 truck-loads of refuse being dumped daily, 100 would be dumped locally and the remaining 230 distributed among the three centralised dumping grounds. It was agreed that the bulldozer should be deployed only where the maximum number of truck-loads of refuse is being dumped. This would be at one of the three centralised dumping grounds. The total number of refuse truck-loads expected at such a dumping ground would be about 100.

The officials suggested that the refuse should be dumped at a low lying area within the zone in order to make the dumping operations economical as well as useful.

The Conservancy Jamadar could be gainfully employed to control the labour and to keep a record of refuse truck-trips at each of the major dumping grounds thus relieving the Assistant Sanitary Inspector of duty. Five posts of filter coolies may be distributed among the three major dumping grounds according to the number of the vehicles which may be visiting from time to time.

As a result of such a streamlining of the administration, 2 Assistant Sanitary Inspectors and 48 sweepers will be rendered surplus, with their wage bill costing Rs. 1,19,900, as worked out by the O&M Division. This surplus staff could then be adjusted for meeting additional staff requirement which may arise due to expansion of the activities of the health department. The foregoing analysis throws certain suggestions for effecting efficiency in the present system. First, rational allocation and utilization of vehicles, used for the disposal of garbage. Second, building bye-laws of the Corporation should make provision for house-to-house dust-bins and community dust-bins for the area. Third, the present arrangement of cleaning the dust-bins once in two weeks is far from adequate. Fourth, there should be clear-cut procedural objectives for the whole operation and allocation of personnel and trucks according to the needs of particular locality and the economic issues involved. Fifth, the programme of converting dry latrines into wet should be taken up on a priority basis.

Food Adulteration and Food Hygiene

The Prevention of Food Adulteration Act enacted by the Parliament in 1954 has made adulteration an offence. This Act is also applicable to Delhi. If one is convicted of adulterating food for the first time he may be sentenced to imprisonment for one year or a fine extending to Rs. 2,000 or both. For the second offence, a person is sentenced to imprisonment which may extend to two years and a fine amounting to not less than Rs. 2,000 can be imposed. For the third and subsequent offences, the sentence is imprisonment which may extend to four years and a fine which may not be less than Rs. 3,000.

According to this Act all the Sanitary Inspectors in the Health Department are authorised Inspectors to analyse food samples. The Headquarters Zonal Health Officer with a group of 8 Food Inspectors is engaged on supervision of foodstuffs. Their services are also available for consultation to operators of establishments and shops. Either reported by public or through direct inspection, the suspected foodstuff is forwarded to the food laboratory for proper analysis. An article of food can be tested by public analysts by payment of the prescribed fee in the Public Health Laboratory. It will be discussed in the following paragraph. Thus inspection, supervision and enforcement of legal action are the three basic components of ensuring unadulterated foodstuffs and clean eatable places.

Public Health Laboratory

The Public Analyst of the Laboratory receives food samples from the New Delhi Municipal Committee, the Cantonment, Railways, Customs Authorities etc. Sometimes public also can forward the samples for chemical analysis on payment of certain prescribed fees. The standards of food and the procedures for carrying out different kinds of analysis are laid down in the Prevention of Food Adulteration Act.

Two trained Senior Chemists, one Assistant Chemist, eight Chemists, one Laboratory Assistant, four Clerks and four Class IV staff are working under the Public Analyst. An impression of the volume of other activities of this laboratory could be gathered from the figures relating to samples given below during the years 1961, 1967 and 1968.

Particulars	1961	1967	1968 (upto December)
Samples received	1,042	2,942	3,788
Samples analysed	811	2,002	3,594
Samples found adulterated	564	603	606

These figures indicate that while the samples received have increased three times during the period 1961 to 1968, the number of samples analysed increased four times and the proportion of samples found adulterated does not indicate much increase. Officials attribute this to the strengthening of the staff position. However, considering the total area and population of the metropolis, the volume of activities seems to be rather moderate.

Although there is an increase in the number of samples analysed, it does not seem to meet fully the requirements ensuring wholesome food for the citizens. A casual observation of eating places makes one believe that not much is being done in the form of testing the foodstuffs effectively.

The Public Analyst, as mentioned earlier, is also entrusted with laboratory testing work of all Corporation hospitals, dispensaries, health centres and maternity and child welfare centres, apart from water testing against bacteriological purity and chlorine content. Prevention and spread of water-borne diseases—all these necessitate inspection and survey of water systems and collection of water samples for analysis in public health laboratory. About 20 samples are collected daily by two Assistants. The Zonal Health Officers send the samples of the non-chlorinated sources of water, such as tube-well, open well and hand pumps.

Nature of Study	1959	1961	1967-68
Pathological investigations	15,830	19,344	40,666
Infectious diseases investigation	6,958	7,354	—
Water samples analysis	6,415	6,430	7,098

The analysis of the above figures suggests a significant expansion of activities in the pathological investigation of the medical cases. This expansion is attributed to two factors, e.g., (i) the laboratory having been brought under the same roof of public health laboratory, and (ii) general awareness of the medical officers and public to avail of pathological investigation of the cases. All these discussions suggest that one laboratory technician, assisting the Public Analyst for water sampling work and one for infection detection are inadequate in identifying and arresting sources of the communicable diseases in the capital.

The facilities of public health laboratory are also used by health department personnel to assist them in diagnosing, treating and controlling communicable diseases. The private physician also uses the laboratory for testing. The laboratory carries bacteriolgical tests for diagnosis of typhoid and paratyphoid fevers, diphtheria, streptococcal infections, basillary dysentery, parasitic infection and ringworm. It analyses water and milk samples taken by the sanitarians. It also conducts testing of food samples for detecting adulterated contents.

Legal Wing

As mentioned earlier the Food Hygiene Section has also a prosecution branch attached to it. The offensive cases in spite of repeated warning are convicted. The official figures of the prosecution cases upto December 1968 are given below :

Nature of Prosecution	1967	1968
Conviction	425	355
Acquittals	246	188
Withdrawn	82	27
Filed in court	16	15
Pending in court	353	253

The figures regarding the nature of punishment awarded to them are as under :

Nature of Punishment	1967	1968
Fine	39	63
Fine and imprisonment	386	291
Only imprisonment	386	1
Total amount of fine realised	Rs. 4,29,329	Rs. 3,65,669

The above figures indicate that the number of cases in which fine was imposed has gone up from 39 to 63, whereas fine and imprisonment declined from 386 to 291. In 1968, about 253 cases were pending in the court. All these are evidence of impractical legal provisions and ineffective court procedures. For instance, the Municipal rules require two eye-witnesses to be present in the court for a particular defaulting case, but in actual practice it is very difficult to find two volunteers to give evidence against their local vendor. Thus the efficiency of action is limited by impractical procedures. Trial of cases by the Mobile Courts through Honorary Magistrates can be conceived as an expeditious method. Intensive sampling for the whole of Delhi area and the Food Inspectors visiting the vulnerable areas to dispose of the unhygienic food products can also help in minimising this evil.

Health Education

Health education has been defined as the "sum of experiences which favourably influence habits, attitudes and knowledge relating to individual, community and racial health." (William 1956 : 169) It is, therefore, necessary to create awareness among people and the community about health needs and problems so that they can utilize available services to the best possible advantage and also help in arresting the spread of diseases. This task is performed by the health education cell. The health education cell of the department is the only focal point of the wide variety of educational programmes carried out by the health department to educate public in usefulness of preventive health information through newspapers, radio and television. Educational material not available through other sources is prepared in the Section. These include slides, posters and pamphlets.

One Cinema Van is attached to the Public Health Section. It carries a microphone for announcement. It covers on an average 375 miles every month. It has a film projector for showing educative films in the medical institutions. It also participates in anti-fly week campaign, anti-smallpox drive and sanitation drive with the Delhi Administration.

This cell is managed by one untrained Publicity Assistant who is attached to the Deputy Health Officer (Public Health) at the headquarters. The Zonal Health Officer also works as health educator at the zonal level.

This study revealed that the Zonal Health Officer did not have any useful publicity material, although he was responsible for health education in the zonal areas. It was pointed out in this connection that health education literature was distributed only in the event of the outbreak of cholera or smallpox epidemic. The staff interviewed at the field level did not attach much value to the publicity material currently used.

Local health education according to Smolensky (1961 : 286) should include :

(a) Preparation of a community to accept its health responsibility.

(b) Community to be informed of its health status, i.e., individual measures for prevention and control of health problems.

(c) Availability of community facilities and services for the prevention and control of health problems, programme and services of the health department.

(d) Community should be participating in coordinated planning and programming for appraisal of community facilities and services, utilization of existing community facilities and services, provision of additional needed community facilities and services.

(e) Community composed of individuals motivated to observe the personal practices conducive to physical, mental and emotional health. The need is more for education in a metropolis with 54.64 per cent illiterate population.

This study reveals that the Corporation has not attached enough importance to this group of clientele. Available equipments and materials for publicity are far from adequate to cover the entire metropolis. The officials interviewed also shared the same views.

Health Statistics Unit

Collection of systematic information alone can provide a sound base for various welfare programmes. Thus, it is most important to gather such an information and properly record it. It is for this purpose the Corporation has its statistical unit. Records and reports must, therefore, be designed to permit qualitative and quantitative analysis of the health services to individuals, families and the community and the periodical appraisal of the health department programme (Johnson 1953 : 1).

The term 'vital records' or health statistics normally refers to birth and death certificates. Health statistics of the New Delhi Municipal Committee, Delhi Municipal Corporation and Cantonment area are compiled by the Health Statistics Unit of the Corporation. Furthermore, this unit is also responsible for the administrative recording on the basis of the reports obtained from different health sections and the Zonal Units for internal reporting.

The unit is managed by one Statistical Officer, one Statistical Assistant, two Statistical Collectors and three Compilers. The Sanitary Inspectors at the zonal level also act as registrar for births and deaths.

Control of Communicable Diseases

Administrative measures The administrative measures to be taken against epidemics depend upon the epidemiological characteristics of the disease. Generally, they are of two kinds, (i) permanent and (ii) seasonal. The permanent measures were firstly control of dangerous and offensive trades, provision of protected water, the enforcement of compulsory vaccination, the destruction of malarial larvae, rat proofing and the maintenance of sanitary condition. When cholera broke out, the authorities deputed vaccinators to distribute cholera pills. Disinfection of infected places meant the distribution of sticks of camphors and sulphur.

Tuberculosis

The Corporation created a separate T.B. Control Section, in 1961, to coordinate anti-T.B. work. All diagnosed cases in different institutions or general hospitals are notified to the T.B. Control Section where a live T.B. index is maintained. Admission to T.B. Hospital is governed by the Admission Board, headed by the Health Officer.

During the Third Five Year Plan period, about Rs. 20 lakhs were allotted for the B.C.G. campaign in rural and urban areas and about 7,80,500 persons were reported to be vaccinated in 1967-68.

The T.B. Control Officer, in the rank of Deputy Health Officer, is in charge of the section and is assisted by other Medical Officers in charge of the Urban T.B. Clinics run by the Corporation. Following is an account of the existing facilities for T.B. treatment in Delhi.

TABLE V.2

Statement of the existing facilities for T.B. treatment in Delhi

Institutions	No. of Beds	Management
Silver Jubilee T.B. Hospital (for Kingsway Camp)	863	M.C.D.
Municipal T.B. Clinic, S.P. Mukherjee Marg (for Civil Lines and Subzimandi area)		do
T.B. Clinic, Shahdara (for West of Jamuna)		do
Moti Bagh (for West of Delhi)		do
Jhandewalan Kilokari	22	do
Narela (for rural area)	22	do
Kishanganj (for the same area)		do
Mehrauli T.B. Clinic (for the same area)	450	T.B. Association of India
New Delhi T.B. Clinic		do
Ramakrishna Mission T.B. Clinic (Karol Bagh)		Ramakrishna Mission

Source : Corporation's Administration Report 1962-63 and the Hospital Review Committee Report, 1968

The Silver Jubilee T.B. Hospital has an outdoor section catering to the Civil Lines and part of Subzimandi. The Mehrauli T.B. Clinic has an outdoor clinic, looking after the cases for Mehrauli area. Thus it appears that while other parts of Delhi are by and large covered by the institutional centres, South Delhi and the Delhi City area are yet to be covered, resulting in a large number of undiagnosed T.B. cases being transferred to general hospitals, thereby creating health hazards to non-T.B. patients there.

Smallpox Eradication Scheme

The smallpox eradication programme of the Corporation was started with grant-in-aid from the Central Government in 1962. House-to-house enumeration of population to ensure complete coverage of immunization, proper supervision through vaccination inspectors, vaccinators and lady vaccinators and by providing storage facilities for the vaccine, are some of the services provided. In 1967-68, about 1,40,830 persons were primarily vaccinated, 8,70,208 re-vaccinated and 62,328 were mass vaccinated by the flying squad.

TABLE V.3

Trend of incidence of Smallpox in relation to deaths in Delhi Union Territory

Year	Cases	Deaths
1960	1,096	215
1961	912	217
1962	177	44
1963	508	103
1964	91	20
1965	296	56
1966	407	77
1967	306	68
1968	450	110
1969	65	13
1970	90	18

Source : Compiled from the records of the Corporation—Health Statistics Department

Incidence of 110 death cases in 1968 suggests the existence of the problem to a certain extent. The relationship of death per case is somewhat constant 1 : 4 or 1 : 5. In 1970, from the cases reported from Jhuggi colonies in Wazirpur, Lajpat Nagar and Rana Pratap Bagh, it appears that although the incidence has come down, the proportion of deaths remains more or less the same.

It is, however, interesting to note that the incidence of the disease is higher among the unvaccinated. Secondly, fatality is higher in the unvaccinated group. Thirdly, children under the age of 10 are most affected. For instance, 64.3 per cent of cases were below the age of 10 years. In contrast, among the vaccinated group 189 cases (62% out of 302) occurred in the age group between 10 to 30. The staff of 110 vaccinators of the Corporation Health Department (majority of whom are temporary) is far from adequate to cover 25,000 population per vaccinator. By that standard the Corporation needs 63 more vaccinators.

It was observed that 14 per cent of the cases of smallpox were imported from the adjoining States. The infection brought from outside leads to local outbursts, particularly in slum areas where the infection is generally imported from the neighbouring States. It is evident that the metropolis cannot control the incidence of smallpox, unless the neighbouring States also have a similar immunization programme.

Malaria Control

Malaria Control Programme which was started in 1946, got further momentum with the onset of the National Malaria Control Programme in 1953, which developed into the Malaria Eradication Programme in 1958. Till 1968-69, the malaria eradication scheme was in consolidation phase. About 500 surveillance workers were engaged under one Malaria Control Officer. The scheme is now reduced to maintenance phase and the total strength employed is much below the previous strength.

Table V.4 indicates that the incidence of diseases, either imported or local, is oscillating. The increase in incidence in the year 1968 has been attributed to the Central Government decision to withdraw the staff. The Corporation

TABLE V.4

Incidence of Malaria during 1962-68

Year	Imported	Local	Total
1962	21	162	183
1963	33	28	61
1964	14	5	19
1965	5	2	7
1966 (upto August)	4	2	6
1968	100	8	108

Source : Annual Budget, D.M.C., 1969-70

is reported to have requested the Central Government for the extension of the "consolidation phase" on the ground that the mosquitoes are still rampant in Delhi. The Central Government has actually decided to grant Rs. 5 lakhs instead of Rs. 12 lakhs, and dismiss 500 workers as a part of economy measure.

Cholera Control

Budget Report (1967) enumerates a mild breakdown of cholera epidemic in 1966. The cholera cases were all investigated with the aid of National Institute of Communicable Diseases. Cholera inoculation work continues from April to September in Maternity and Child Welfare Centres and municipal dispensaries. The Health Department record shows that the number of inoculators has declined as may be seen from the following data :

Year	Inoculators	Vaccinated	Per 1000 Population
1967	42	4,71,748	308
1968	21	2,69,623	209

Shortage of inoculators and the public apathy towards immunization could be attributed to decline in coverage of population from 308 to 209. However, the current endeavour to integrate all communicable diseases under one Deputy Director could perhaps improve the situation as more workers from other fields could be available for inoculation activity.

School Medical Scheme

Local Health Department contributes to the school health programme by periodically appraising the health of school children, providing health education services and supervising the sanitary facilities of the school.

Many schools cooperate with the staff of the health department in an effort to appraise the health of certain students. Screening in school health programme is routine and simple for the purpose of identifying children needing further examination and diagnosis from qualified specialists. In this way, many disorders can be prevented and deficiencies can be corrected. Screening tests mostly include growth and development, vision and hearing test. Immunizations are also provided for the students who so desire. Observation, deviation and corrections are carefully noted on the students cumulative health record. Consultation, referral to specialist and follow-up are necessary adjunct to the programme. Thus, the school health programme helps in preventing communicable diseases and also in inculcating attitudes conducive to health.

Since 1958, until recently, the School Medical Scheme was attached to the Maternity & Child Welfare Department of the Corporation. The scheme provides initial medical examination of all entrants every three years. Inoculation, vaccination and training in personal hygiene are the services provided through this programme.

Recently the scheme has been introduced in all municipal schools. The scheme has received strong impetus during the last two years with the new Health Officer in 1969. Arrangements are being made to provide hospital beds for the poor school children in Victoria Zanana Hospital.

One paediatrician is in charge of the central school medical scheme with a group of 16 doctors and 2 assistants. Zonal Health Officers are also responsible for school medical inspection for checking up the sanitary environments of schools.

Medical Relief

We have already mentioned that in the post-independence era, Delhi received a number of refugees from West Punjab, who were given shelter in three main camps, Kingsway, Tibbia College in Karol Bagh and at Shahdara. Subsequently, townlets were developed by the Rehabilitation Ministry to accommodate these uprooted families. There were four core areas; in the south this was formed by Nizamuddin, Lajpat Nagar, Kalkaji and Malviya Nagar; in the west two Rajendra Nagars, three Patel Nagars, Moti Nagar, Ramesh Nagar and Tilak Nagar; in the north Kingsway which spread to Timarpur, Roopnagar, Kamla Nagar, Jawahar Nagar and Shakti Nagar; in the east Gandhi Nagar in Shahdara. During this period the old city including Chandni Chowk, Subzi Mandi, Sadar Bazar, Sarai Rohilla, Jhandewalan, Paharganj to Shakurbasti, along old Rohtak Road rapidly filled up to bursting point. The limits of the city are now reaching beyond Kailash and Qutab in the south tending to cover Faridabad in the south-east, and beyond Najafgarh in the west. In the eastern side Shahdara has also merged into Ghaziabad.

It is in this context of physical growth of the metropolis, one should study the expansion of medical care services. The Corporation provides all types of specialised, institutional and domiciliary services through its 20 hospitals, 5 public health centres, 34 dispensaries, 5 urban health centres, 5 T.B. clinics, 2 V.D. clinics and 1 leprosy clinic in various geographical areas of the city (see Appendix A.3, for the list of these institutions and about the areas indicated). Apart from these institutions, about 10 private hospitals and 15 dispensaries are receiving grants-in-aid from the Corporation. In 1967-68 the total annual budget for medical relief services was nearly Rs. two crores. During 1969, about 54,53,670 outdoor and 56,606 indoor patients were given institutional care.

Hospitals

The Corporation hospitals are classified into three categories, *viz.*, (i) General Hospital, (ii) Specialised Service Hospital, and (iii) Second-grade or Intermediary Hospital. Besides these three categories of hospitals, health centres in rural and urban areas (as suggested by Bhore Committee), dispensaries and clinics are operating in different parts of the city. These will all be discussed separately. (Table V.5

TABLE V.5

Services provided by the Medical Relief Institutions under Delhi Municipal Corporation

Types of Agencies	No. of Institutions	No. of Beds	Indoor	Outdoor
1. General Hospitals (including Colony Hospitals)	11	770	36,630	20,60,514
2. Specialised Hospitals				
(a) T.B.	1	1,113	4,555	n.a.
(b) Infectious Diseases	1	175	4,794	n.a.
(c) Maternity	2	127	9,105	89,523†
(d) Primary Health Centre	5	47	1,522	1,83,068
3. (a) Dispensaries	37	8	*	27,32,907
(b) Urban Health Centre	3		*	1,94,294
(c) V.D. Clinic	2		*	1,01,487
4. Leprosy Home	2	150†	*	6,160
5. T.B. Clinic	5	*	*	85,717@
	69	2,390	56,606	54,53,670

Source : Corporation Health Intelligence Report, 1969, Health Department, M.C.D.

    * for observation and not for treatment

    † inmates

    @ old and new cases are included

gives the services provided by these institutions with bed position.)

General Hospital

Bara Hindu Rao is a general hospital with 306 beds, providing medical coverage to the entire north Delhi area. It is expected to serve as referral centre for all second-grade hospitals and dispensaries run by the Corporation.

Specialised Hospital

Large hospitals like Infectious Diseases Hospital in Kingsway, Silver Jubilee Tuberculosis Hospital and Victoria Zanana Maternity Hospital are meant for providing specialised services. The standard of these hospitals can be judged by the fact that they are recognised institutions for post-graduate teaching of Delhi University. (See Table V.6 for staff position.)

Second-grade or Intermediate Hospitals

In an attempt to provide medical care in the growing townships in Delhi, a number of small hospitals were set up in the new colonies developed by the Rehabilitation Ministry in post-partition era. There are at present 9 colony hospitals with beds varying from 30 to 50 in each hospital. The areas covered by these hospitals are Tilak Nagar, Patel Nagar, Moti Nagar, T.L. Moti Colony, Shahdara, Janta Staff Railway Zone area, Kalkaji, Malviya Nagar and Lajpat Nagar. The total number of staff of different categories employed in these nine hospitals are : Resident Superintendent two, Surgeon four and Technician one. These hospitals do not have facility for pathological and X-Ray investigations. However, in 1969, these nine colony hospitals have been raised to the Intermediate or Second Class Hospitals to relieve heavy pressure on the General and Specialised Hospitals as suggested by the Gilder Committee in 1956. There has been gradual improvement and upgrading in the standard of these hospitals over a period of time. (See Table V.7 for the expansion of services.)

TABLE V.6

List of major hospitals under Municipal Corporation of Delhi with staff position (as on 1-1-69)

Name of Hospital	Senior Scale Rs. 1150-1500	Senior Specialist Rs. 700-1250	Junior Specialist Rs. 375-900	CAS Grade Rs. 325-800	Total	Indoor beds
Silver Jubilee T.B. Hospital	1	3	3	26	33	1,113
Hindu Rao Hospital	1	12	6	27	46	306
Victoria Zanana Hospital		1	6	13	20	175
I.D. Hospital		2	1	9	12	165
Mrs. Girdharilal Maternity Hospital		—	2	4	6	97
General Hospital Shahdara		2	7	5	14	50
Total	2	20	25	84	131	1,906

The figures above suggest that the number of doctors is not proportionate to indoor beds, as for example, Hindu Rao Hospital has 33 doctors for 1,113 patients or six doctors for 97 patients in Girdharilal Maternity Hospital. It could be pointed out that Hindu Rao and other hospitals have a great load of outdoor patients, which is more than indoor (see earlier table) beds, whereas T.B. or I.D. Hospital has no provision for outdoor patients. Thus the ratio of doctors to patients comes to the same in all hospitals under the Municipal Corporation of Delhi.

TABLE V.7

Expansion of Corporation Medical Care Services during 1961-1968

Name of Hospital	Type	Bed Strength		Area Served	Expenditure (in lakhs)	
		1961	1968		1961	1968
Hindu Rao*	General	127	306	5.2 lakh population of North Delhi. Referral centre for all DMC Hospitals	6.92	26.00
I.D. Hospital	Special	125	165	Whole of Union Territory of Delhi and neighbourhood	3.02	5.89
Victoria Zanana*	Special Women		185	Walled city of Delhi		11.69
Girdharilal Shahdara	Maternity		97	Delhi City		4.35
	General		50	Shahdara		1.26
Silver Jubilee T.B.*	Special	263	1,113	Serves as referral centre for 8 T.B. Clinics, Delhi		32.00
Colony Hospital	General	125	289	Kalkaji, Moti Nagar, Malviya Nagar, Tilak Nagar, Patel Nagar, Timarpur, Kingsway Camp, Shahdara		11.14

*Training in medicine imparted.
The table above is a pointer to the fact that the newly developed areas and colonies in City, Shahdara and West Delhi area are still outside the coverage of the Corporation hospitals; in other words, the residents there have to travel a long way to avail health services.

Following the suggestions of various committees like Bhore, Mudaliar and Rao, the Corporation has opened five urban health centres in recent years. The basic objective of the Urban Health Centre is to provide medical care to the areas devoid of medical facilities of any type.

Expansion of Services

The hospitals and dispensaries have considerably grown in size in recent years, as brought out in the Gilder Committee Report, 1955. The Gilder Committee recommended opening of more centres and upgrading of Hindu Rao Hospital for the North Zone and Shahdara hospital for Eastern Zone. Of the nine colony hospitals, Shahdara is being gradually raised to General Hospital. Urban Health Centres have started functioning. Although there is an expansion of medical services, yet there is no substantial evidence to support that these have been equitably distributed. Sometimes the objectives of some centres are nullified due to overlapping. For example, the Urban Health Centre in Defence Colony, housed in a magnificent building, fails to draw even adequate clients. This may be attributed mainly to two factors : (i) the area is adequately served by two big institutions, like Safdarjang Hospital and All India Medical Institute Hospital on the one hand and Mool Chand Hospital on the other hand; (ii) secondly, the public are today drawn to the more sophisticated medical institutions having better supplies of drugs and other facilities. Thus, the creation of services without regard to the needs of the area results in waste of resources. This is an example of defective planning of services.

Allopathic Dispensaries

In addition to the hospitals, the rural and urban areas are covered by 34 urban and 11 rural dispensaries. The services provided by the dispensaries are outdoor treatment and referral to hospitals. The number of patients attending these clinics has gradually increased (see Table V.8) in case of urban areas, but there is decline in case of rural areas. However, it is difficult to offer any explanation for the same.

TABLE V.8

Trend of Service by Allopathic Dispensaries

| | Year 1961 | | Year 1968 | |
	Urban	Rural	Urban	Rural
New Cases	12,20,715	2,93,769	12,94,051	3,56,247
Old Cases	15,41,277	2,26,131	14,38,856	(total)

A sum of rupees 17,38,945 was spent in 1967-68. The staff includes 62 Civil Assistant Surgeons Grade I, doctors and 93 dressers. Thus, it is evident that the number of centres is on the increase, irrespective of the quality of service.

Specialised Dispensaries

Corporation runs 2 V.D. clinics, one leprosy home and clinic in Shahdara. Besides these clinics, the charitable medical institutions also receive grants.

Primary Health Centres

Corporation runs five primary health centres as a part of integrated rural health programme. It is intended that the primary health centres could provide preventive as well as curative services and school health services in the rural area. A centre runs a six-bedded hospital for providing domiciliary and institutional care. One Civil Assistant Surgeon, one Family Welfare Worker, one Auxiliary Midwife and 2 nurses are the sanctioned staff for the centres.

One Lady Doctor is also attached with the Centre for Family Planning work. Both doctors posted in the area are expected to cover 21,000 population, whereas in other States, the population covered by such centres is much larger (for example, 50,000 in Maharashtra).

The transport problem with old rigid procedure of its maintenance further hampers the extension activities of the Health Officer in the Primary Centre. For example, petrol is required to be filled in from Jhandewalan, fifteen miles away, whereas petrol pump is already located within five miles of the Primary Health Centre. Thus, it is revealed that administrative rules and procedures hindered role performance rather than facilitating it.

The Corporation could perhaps do well by introducing better inspection and supervision system with a view to removing the administrative problems of the Health Centre doctors. That the Health Centres could hardly carry on the preventive and curative work simultaneously was also observed by others (Takulia et al. 1968). This study also shows that doctors lay greater emphasis on curative rather than preventive services in the primary health centres. Therefore, there seems to be urgent need to have a rethinking about the programme.

Indigenous Medicine

India has a long tradition of providing medical relief through Unani and Ayurvedic Systems of Medicine. The Corporation also provides indigenous system of medical service through its dispensaries and an Ayurvedic Hospital (389 beds), in addition to its allopathic dispensaries and hospitals.

TABLE V.9

Beneficiaries from Indigeneous Systems of Medicine (1966-1968)

Year	Ayurvedic	Unani	Homoeopathic	Total
1966	23,69,173	6,36,567	1,47,337	31,53,472
1967	23,10,605	4,74,999	98,469	28,84,073
1968	23,57,738	5,66,206	95,262	30,19,206

It is indicated that in the indigenous system of medicine demand for Ayurvedic remains almost constant whereas the demand for Unani is on the increase and so also for Homoeopathic. The respondents felt that people still preferred Allopathic medicine to indigenous system of medicine. They may try other systems only as a substitute.

As regards the staff, the Deputy Director of Indigenous Medicine is in charge of the entire section. He is assisted by 13 Hakims, 6 Vaids, one allopathic doctor and 67 compounders and 33 nurses. One Pharmacy Officer is in charge of medical stores of the indigenous medicine. About Rs. 12,04,700 is being spent on the staff. It is worth noting that the New Delhi Municipal Committee has expanded its Ayurvedic centres from two to five during the period.

Medical Stores

The supply of medicine and equipments for diagnosis and treatment constitutes an important element for medical relief. The Medical Stores Unit under direct control of the Deputy Health Officer (Medical Care) is responsible for procurement and supply of medicines and equipments.

Interview with the officials concerned revealed that the production was actually in the hands of the private firms. The usual procedure is to prepare a standardised list of drugs for use in the hospital and store them in medical stores. The practice to enter into direct contract for the supply of drugs also exists. However, at times certain drugs are supplied to the stores which were not much in demand in the previous year. There are occasions when useful drugs are found short in supply.

The common practice is to supply on the basis of previous year's consumption. The need for medical care is such that it becomes difficult to predict the requirement just like any other department stores. Sometimes popularity of a doctor in a particular dispensary or prevalence of a disease in epidemic form boost up the demand for a particular medicine, thus creating shortage of supply of that particular medicine in the stores.

There are cases where owing to procedural delays allotted amount remains unspent. For example, in South Delhi Zone during 1968-69, out of Rs. 2.40 lakhs allotted for medicines in the allopathic dispensaries only Rs. 1.55 lakhs could be spent. The health officials themselves were frustrated with this state of affairs.

In order to get over some of these problems it was suggested that the Assistant Zonal Commissioner should be empowered to send indent for total requirement of medicines and equipment for the entire zone, after consultation with all medical officers of the area. Each zone should have a future plan of supplies in consultation with the dispensaries and the medical officers.

It was also pointed out that the Central Stores need to be administratively strengthened by placing one medical personnel effectively to work under the Deputy Health Officer. The present practice of one Assistant dealing with medical stores is considered to be inadequate and inefficient.

Problems of the Present Organisation

The provision of medical relief for the members of a community is a complex process, for their needs vary widely. Therefore, it calls for an effective and well coordinated network of services, under the charge of a unified authority. But this is not the case with the metropolis, where services are managed by different authorities.

Historically, the health services in different zones of Delhi have developed gradually, without regard to health needs of the city as a whole. Consequently, there is wide disparity in the services available in different areas.*

Following the Gilder Committee suggestion, the Corporation has attempted to incorporate preventive services like immunization with maternity and child welfare and family planning centres. Domiciliary services are confined to maternity and tuberculosis cases. The Gilder Committee recommended for the integrated Health Centres linking peripheral services with poly-clinics, main sector hospitals and the specialised hospital on the principle of one health centre for 20,000 population of Delhi. The Delhi Master Plan projecting 80 lakhs of population by 1980 proposed for one general hospital for every 25,000 population and one specialised big hospital for each planning division. The Municipal Corporation had accepted the recommendation in principle. How far the existing resources, procedure and structure of the organisation are conducive to implement these policies needs to be examined. Population in Delhi has already reached over 40 lakhs by 1971 Census.

According to the authorities, the problems of medical care are multifarious in Delhi. The catchment area for hospital is

* Civil Lines and New Delhi Municipal Committee had better staffing pattern as they were abode of civilians and government officials.

not confined to the Union Territory of Delhi alone, but it extends 80 to 100 miles around.

According to the authorities, the hospital beds are, to a large extent, occupied by patients coming from adjoining States of Haryana, U.P. and Rajasthan for better medical care. Consequently, the hospitals in Delhi are always overcrowded. Thus the Delhi hospitals have to cater to much larger numbers than they can actually cope with.

On the administrative side there is the problem of acquiring regular supply of equipments and stores. For example, Hindu Rao Hospital needed 31 coolers, Silver Jubilee T.B. Hospital 24 and Girdharilal Maternity Hospital 6 for operation theatres. The hospital authorities had sent their requisitions but the administration took time to ask firms to supply coolers. The firms had then refused to supply coolers because the demand went much later than the beginning of the season. As a result, the surgeons of three major hospitals had refused to operate on patients for the operation theatres were not adequately equipped. Similar types of instances were mentioned by other hospital authorities to the author. It was pointed out that blankets were supplied much after the winter had set in.

Need for Coordination

In the event of constant gap between the adequacy of equipment and the needs of public health, it is necessary to bring about coordination of the existing services for fuller utilisation of services. The Hospital Review Committee, 1968, commenting on uncoordinated efforts in Delhi Medical Care services stated that two big institutions, Safdarjang Hospital (1,148 beds plus 174 basic nets) and All India Institute of Medical Sciences Hospital (560 beds) with a total bed strength of 2,000, have developed on either side of the road in South Delhi. The Gobind Ballabh Pant Hospital is located in the already overcrowded premises of Irwin Hospital with 1,063 beds. In contrast to this, West or North Delhi area shows hardly any hospital coverage.

Distribution of Hospitals

Uneven distribution of hospital facilities is further commented upon by the Hospital Review Committee : "There is not equitable distribution of hospital facilities in Delhi. Existing hospitals have expanded and continue to expand without any consideration of the needs of the population in various sectors. Unsatisfactory communication system in certain parts of Delhi, particularly in the outlying colonies, add further hazards to the people." The officials pointed out that research and investigation of the teaching hospitals at times refuse admission to the emergency cases thereby creating great suffering to the ordinary public and advantage to the 'privileged class'.

The present distribution of existing hospitals in Delhi in relation to its needs, as worked out by the Master Plan, is as follows :

Area	Existing	Proposed	Need
Old City	1	1	1
Karol Bagh	—	1	1
Civil Lines	1	1	2
New Delhi	3	1	4
Shahdara	1	6	7
South Delhi	2	2	2
West Delhi	—	5	5
West Jamuna Canal	—	4	4

It is, therefore, evident that of the 26 general hospitals needed for Delhi, only 8 exist today. The position in West Delhi, Shahdara, Jamuna Canal area seems to be worst.

The location of maternity and child welfare centres also indicates that the principle of regionalisation has not been followed. Thus structurally and organisationally medical services are not even providing integrated services, what to speak of total coverage.

The above discussion reveals that since the Gilder Committee Report and the K.N. Rao Committee Report on Hospital Reorganisation, no substantial improvement in the organisation of Delhi Corporation hospitals has come up, except upgrading of the Hindu Rao Hospital. With emergency declared in 1962, a drastic cut in welfare services also stifled the progress of all welfare programmes in the small hospitals in the colonies. The development of a large number of dispensaries and development of quality of services in the existing ones were some of the suggestions offered by the staff interviewed. Some of the officials suggested that the private practitioners should be allowed to attend to medical care on contract basis for the Corporation. They felt, it would reduce overcrowding in dispensaries and help relieve the acute problem of medical care in Delhi.

As the health department is directly or indirectly responsible for providing a proper standard of medical care for the metropolis, the Corporation would do well to consider some of these proposals. They may also improve the outdoor facilities and provide immunization services for better integration of public health with medical care programme.

The descriptive analysis above shows that the services have expanded but the performance is inadequate as compared to the needs of the metropolis. In the absence of any standardised method to evaluate the medical services, it is rather difficult to make an assessment of the effectiveness of the services provided by the Department. But surely there is enough scope for administrative improvement.

Some of the main shortfalls in the existing programmes are :

(1) Ineffective machinery to implement the health legislations. Lack of judicial support to carry out the health programme efficiently. The cases are usually heard for months together without any decision being given.

(2) Archaic administrative procedures of the past century are strictly followed in case of health department without any attempt to take up programme on priority basis. Services are undertaken without making study of the different areas to achieve maximum utility to maximum number of people.

(3) Coverage is far from adequate in relation to needs.

(4) Procedures are complicated and time-consuming without having any consideration of the convenience of the citizen resulting in public hostility. Lack of coordination among departments and units creates delay.

(5) In the absence of supportive social services to follow up the cases attending the department, some programmes although appear attractive on surface, prove to be infructuous. For example, in the absence of properly developed blind school, handicapped homes or school for mentally retarded children, these children cannot be treated through the school health programme. Similarly in the absence of rehabilitation programme, the patients discharged after treatment will not be easily restored to the society. In the absence of follow-up and rehabilitative programme, temporary medical care activities prove superficial and short-statured. They may create some impression at the outset, but leave no far-reaching effects. The health programme detached from other social service activities cannot ensure proper results.

The foregoing observations indicate that management of the programme needs to have an effective administrative machinery to implement the health bye-laws. The personnel working in the field should have proper legislative support. Any violation should be resented by the Corporation.

In short, the health service programmes, in order to be effective, have to be so designed as to accommodate and respond to the changing needs of the community. This can be accomplished only when the institutional framework, within which these services are managed, is open and flexible. The field of health administration is dynamic.

CHAPTER VI

Activity Analysis : Family Planning

We have earlier made reference to Family Planning and other constituent units of the Health Department of the Corporation. In view of the special characteristics of the Family Planning Administration, it is desirable to deal with it separately in the present chapter. Family Planning is the latest entry among the various wings of the health department in the year 1968. It is attached to maternity and child health section of the health department.

Objectives of Family Planning

1. Ultimate programme impact objectives :
   (a) To ensure welfare of the family as a whole.
   (b) To reduce birth rate from 40/1000 to 25/1000 by 1975.
2. Intermediate objective—community's acceptance of a small family norm.
3. Programme execution objectives.

While fixing programme execution objectives of family planning, it would be convenient to consider three important particulars of the programme, *viz.*, (i) professional services, (ii) the community, the recipient of these services, and (iii) the administrative organisation through which services are rendered to the community. These three major variables are interacting within the structure of the family planning. The changes in any one or more of them may have repercussions on the other components of the programme.

    4. Administrative objectives :
        (a) Organisational set up with respect to personnel and their interrelationship.
        (b) Organisational set up with respect to facilities and the material resources.
        (c) Organisational set up with respect to finance.
    5. Performance objectives.

This is to be broken up into steps like planning, decision-making, communication, supervision, coordination, recording, evaluation and research.

Historical Background

In order to understand the programme in its larger perspective, it is necessary to discuss the history of the maternity and child health services in India. This is so, because in Delhi as elsewhere Family Planning Programme is considered to be an integral part of the Family Welfare Programme, starting with maternal and child welfare programme. However, the early history of maternity and child welfare does not show much evidence of family planning activities as a part of their programme. Health visitors were the main pivot of the child health and maternal education programme.

While the former provides child health and maternal education service the latter provides midwifery service. The Bhore Committee (1946) recommended family planning programme for population control as a part of the M.C.H. programme. Phase two of the Maternity and Child Health movement in India started with the institution of the First Five Year Plan. During the First and Second Five Year Plan periods Maternity and Child Health Centres were practising their regular activities. Family Planning was then taken up on action cum-experiment basis, in certain selected parts of India.

The experiment being successful a separate Family Planning Board was set up at the Centre.

Third phase of the movement started during the Third Five Year Plan. In 1966 integration of maternal and child health with Family Planning was prescribed as official objective of the Government of India. With extension approach to Family Planning in 1962-63, a full-fledged department of Family Planning was established at the Centre in 1967. In 1968, the fifth National Family Planning Council meeting held in Nainital emphasised the need for Family Planning Programme through the country's health services offered to the community. These two programmes were placed under single administration at national, state and local level. It was decided to open one centre per 30,000 people all over India. Family Planning thus received importance towards the end of the Third Five Year Plan and since then with opening up of facilities for practical work it has made rapid progress. Voluntary associations and the municipal government became responsible for providing full complement of maternal and child health services as a part of overall programme.

As seen earlier, provision of health care is the main responsibility of State and to some extent Municipal Corporation. The national Government through the Ministry of Health has been performing advisory and supportive functions. The Union Government, for example, has first initiated malaria and smallpox eradication and then Family Planning.

State and Corporation authorities fully collaborate with the national programmes. Similar has been the case with Family Planning. States have been consulted for launching and carrying on these programmes. There are two divisions in the Central Ministry of Health, namely, Directorate General of Health Services and Department of Family Planning and Maternal and Child Health.

Maternity and Child Health care, until 1968 located in the Directorate of Health Services, was transferred to the Family Planning Department of the Ministry of Health with a M.C.H. Advisor on Family Planning. The programme then became "Family Planning and Maternal Child Health".

In Family Planning 99% is financed by the Central Government, whereas total Maternal and Child Care is financed by the State Government. Central Government has made funds available to the States, Primary Health Centre and Municipal Corporation.

The manpower pattern in the Family Planning Department in the States includes a Deputy Director, necessary administrative staff, education and information unit and a unit for operation and evaluation.

Primary Health Unit

The technical personnel of primary health centre before the advent of the Family Planning Programme consisted of a health officer, a public health nurse, two midwives and a sanitary inspector. Three auxiliary nurse midwives were posted in sub-centres within the block.

There are plans for providing buildings for sub-centres, but very few buildings have been constructed so far. The Family Planning Programme provides for an additional physician, usually a lady doctor, a lady health visitor and additional auxiliary nurse midwives in the proportion of one auxiliary nurse midwife per 10,000 population. Besides, an extension health educator for the block and a field worker (Family Planning Assistant) per 20,000 population are planned.

The personnel of the health unit are all engaged, to some extent, in Family Planning activities which range from general education of the people to the individual persuasion of eligible couples to adopt family planning practices. The lady doctor is responsible for inserting the UCD and the male medical officer for vasectomy operations. The nursing personnel are responsible for motivating individuals, for dispensing contraceptives and follow-up of individuals, who have had loop insertions or tubal ligations.

Delhi

In Delhi, Maternity and Child Welfare had been the main prerogative of the local self government in the early part of this century. Several Municipal Committees prior to 1958 used to run their own maternal and child health care programme.

ORGANIZATION SET UP OF FAMILY PLANNING SECTION OF HEALTH
DEPARTMENT DELHI MUNICIPAL CORPORATION

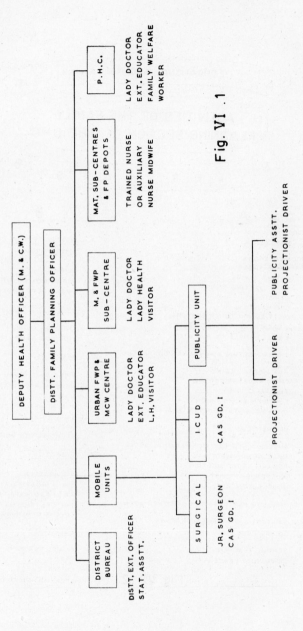

Fig. VI .1

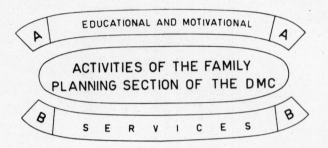

EDUCATIONAL AND MOTIVATIONAL

ACTIVITIES OF THE FAMILY PLANNING SECTION OF THE DMC

A   B

S E R V I C E S

A

1. MASS MEDIA

   FILM SHOWS
   MAGIC SHOWS
   PUPPET SHOWS
   MASS MEETING
   EXHIBITION
   CINEMA STILL
   DISTRIBUTION OF LITERATURE
   8 BACK PANELS OF DTU BUSES
   8 BACK PANELS OF BUS STOP

2. GROUP MEETING & PERSONAL CONTACT :

   ANTI-NATAL CLINIC
   CHILD WELFARE CENTRE
   GENERAL CLINIC HOUSES
   (OFFICES BANKS UNIONS
   OUT-PATIENTS OF HOSPITALS ETC.)

3. IN THE FIELD :

   SURVEY - (TO GET MOTIVATIONAL SURVEYS)
   MALE GROUP MEETINGS
   FEMALE GROUP MEETINGS
   INDEPENDENT CONTACT
   COUPLE CONTACT

4. THROUGH PARTICIPATION OF OTHER AGENTS :

   SANITARY & OTHER HEALTH STAFF
   SOCIAL EDUCATION STAFF

   SCHOOL TEACHER
   COMMUNITY LEADERS

B

I. DISTRIBUTION OF CONTRACE PTIVE THROUGH

   CLINICS
   DURING HOME VISIT
   LOCAL DEPOT HOLDER

II. I.U.C.D. STORES

   THROUGH CLINICS
   THROUGH CAMPS

III. VASECTOMY

   HINDU RAO HOSPITAL
   SHAHDARA GENERAL HOSPITAL
   CAMPS
   PUBLIC HEALTH CENTRE
   COLONY HOSPITAL
   REFERRED TO NEAREST
   STERLISATION UNIT

IV. TUBECTOMY

   V.Z.HOSPITAL
   G.L.M. HOSPITAL
   HINDU RAO HOSPITAL
   THE CENTRES MAY ALSO REFER
   TO ANY OTHER HOSPITAL

V. FOLLOW UP

   FAMILY PLANNING CONTRACEPTIVE
   USER
   I.U.C.D. CASES
   STERLISATION OPERATION CASES

Fig. VI .2

Midwives were mainly responsible for domiciliary delivery cases, while health visitors were like health educators. They used to preach for family planning along with other personal hygiene. But it was neither based on any policy nor supported by any legislation. Consequently, the programme was of a piecemeal nature.

In 1958, the Maternity and Child Health services of the different municipal committees were coordinated under the Deputy Director of Maternity and Child Health Section of the Corporation. As late as 1968, the Family Planning Officer was appointed at the headquarters. But she was kept under the control of the Maternity and Child Health Section. Thus, Family Planning Programme developed as an offshoot of the Maternal and Child Health Section of the Corporation (see Fig. VI.I).

In Delhi Administration, Family Planning Programme is coordinated by Programme Coordinator, who is of the rank of Deputy Director of Health Services, acting as the Chairman of the Implementation Committee for Delhi State. A monthly evaluation meeting of twenty agencies engaged in Family Planning Programme in Delhi Union Territory is held to evaluate and plan the activities and programmes. Health Department of the Corporation is one of the 20 agencies actively engaged in Family Planning Programme. For activities of the Family Planning Section, see Fig. VI.2.

Family Planning Programme, erstwhile managed by the Directorate of Health Services at the State level, has been given over to the Corporation maternity and child health section since 1968. One District Family Planning Officer with the sanctioned cadre of family planning medical and paramedical staff man the programme. Of 64 full-fledged Maternity and Child Health Centres in Delhi, more than half have so far been converted into Family Planning Welfare Centres.

A comprehensive Maternity and Child Health and Family Planning Programme should include : ante-natal care, supply of nutrients to mothers in the last trimester of pregnancy, iron and folic acid tablets administration to prevent anemia, anti-tetanus injection to prevent tetanus, post-natal care, nursing mother craft, child nutrition, immunization, family planning, primary vaccination to the child, school health etc.

Coverage

The expansion of the programme during the 1958-1968 decade may be seen as under :

	1958	1961	1968
No. of Centres	52	55	68
No. of Sub-Centres	17	27	32
Birth rate per 1,000	32.4	27.76	30.9
Deliveries conducted at home	23,312	—	—
Home visits	68,223	2,56,408	2,08,908

There has been gradual increase in Maternity and Child Welfare Centres. Although the number of sub-centres has increased almost by 50%, it has not kept pace with the increase in population which has increased by 60 per cent. Decline in deliveries conducted by the Lady Health Visitor at home is attributed to increasing preference for hospital delivery. The number of home visits comes to 3,560, short by 40 visits on the scale prescribed by the F.C.H. Committee. On the other hand, workload for each visit has rather increased with Family Planning. The budget estimates of the Corporation do not make any separate provision for Maternity and Child Welfare Section making the reviewing of the programme difficult. However, a zonal distribution of budget for 1968-69 and 1969-70 in the Maternity and Child Welfare Centres (appended to the Report), shows that allocation on establishment varies from 2.15 and 2.30 in City Zone and Civil Lines to 0.73 and 0.85 in Paharganj. Thus, these Centres are unevenly located. Moreover, they have been developed without regard to the growing population. While Shahdara, Paharganj and Karol Bagh areas have expanded and got overcrowded, the Maternity and Child Health Centres have not increased proportionately.

Practices

Observation of the records suggests that condom and foam tablets are the most popular methods in Corporation centres.

Consumers' pattern (1968-69) reveals that condoms were used in 5,24,690 cases, diaphragms in 2,117 cases, jellies in 6,749 cases, foam tablets in 13,069, vasectomy in 1,905, tubectomy in 102 and IUCD in 3,912 cases.

The statistical records suggest that about 48 per cent population has already been covered. Efforts have to be mobilized to cover the remaining 52 per cent of the population. It is evident that sterilisation and IUCD methods have little impact in Corporation area.

TABLE VI.1
Decline in Family Planning Practices

Year	No. of Sterilisation Cases	No. of IUCD Cases	Total expenditure on the Programme
1965-66	514	10,597	*
1966-67	221	3,780	*
1967-68	7,115	2,873	Rs. 1,51,374
1968-69	3,007	3,912	Rs. 1,75,000

*In the absence of separate head of account for Family Planning, this information was not available.

Personnel

The staff employed for the purpose can be classified into two categories in terms of their competence and skill for handling Family Planning activities :

(i) Professional and Technical : Doctors, Auxiliary Nurse Midwives, Health Visitors, Health Educators, Statistical Staff and Family Welfare Workers and Store Keepers.
(ii) Non-professional Administrative, Executive, Field and General Service Staff.

The Lady Medical Officer in the Family Planning Centre is mainly responsible for developing the Family Planning Programme. She is expected to form family planning committee of important persons of the area and act as the secretary of the committee. She is responsible to administer family planning practices. The Family Planning Extension Educators primarily work as a liaison between the Centre and the community. The Lady Health Visitor is primarily to assist the Medical Officer in organising Maternity and Child Health and Family Planning services. She is supposed to contact the local leaders, private practitioners and representatives of other welfare agencies and also to work as Extension Educator in the latter's absence. Family Welfare Worker is required to collect necessary data to keep the community informed about the programme and plan programmes in keeping with the needs. Auxiliary Nurse Midwife is expected to assist the Medical Officer in follow-up work, pre-natal, post-natal, infant and pre-school care. The Medical Officers so far engaged in management of pre-natal, post-natal and delivery cases are now entrusted with two important additional tasks, (a) loop insertion, tubectomy and (b) Family Planning campaign. This dual role entrusted to them places heavy reponsibilities on them for not merely carrying out their work but also supervising the work of the field staff.

Problems

Birth rate in Delhi Corporation area is 30 per thousand, against the target of 25 per thousand. It was also observed that 52 per cent of the population remains to be covered. It is, therefore, evident that the authorities have not been able to fulfil the set targets. Thus, there is need to tone up the administration of family planning practices.

Motivation

Lack of motivation at top level of administration was indicated as the major bottleneck in the effective implementation of the programme. Discussions with the field staff reveal that the top executives give only lip service to the programme and it gets low priority. It is well evidenced by the fact that the department is housed in a small dingy room. Similarly, in the hospitals, Family Planning cases receive low priority in getting beds. "Everyone takes us as an intruder", was the reaction of a Family Planning doctor. Another doctor remarked : "Our midwives still consider counting of heads (delivery) is more significant than popularising family planning practices." It is interesting to note that observations and discussions revealed that the IUCD as a method was not well accepted by the staff. The Medical Officer, assigned to perform extension work for motivational purpose, also resented the new role of community doctor, their dignity and conventional prestige to visit families and educate them on current health practices (Mitchell 1969). The medical education in our conventional form has inherent contradiction in this practice.

Training

There is, however, a regular arrangement of sending the unqualified staff for training in the Delhi Administration Family Planning Training Centre. As regards the trained mid-wives and health visitors, the problems are mostly of the quality of training. Bonafides of a short duration course to equip a worker to take up this important task was questioned. Duration of training and its quality were under heavy criticism. Close discussion with the staff revealed that the training for a period of a week or two for the midwives was not enough to create the strong determination required for this work.

It is, therefore, suggested that the workers of all categories should be trained in medical aspects at a level adequate for them to comprehend the subject and to be able to answer intelligently questions from the people. It should also provide motivational support.

Likewise the supporting staff and people from other services assisting in the programme, such as the administrators, general practitioners and people working in publicity departments, also lacked motivation. Thus there is need to orient the staff and motivate them for the work expected of them.

Relationship among Medical Officers

The present organisational set up provides for one medical officer at the headquarters, zonal and primary health centre level but the Family Planning Officer is in charge of Family Planning Programme. Being the solitary officer at zonal or

Primary Health Centre and Corporation level it is difficult for her to exercise control over the subordinate staff and gain the confidence of the clientele. The other medical officers of the Family Planning do not take interest in family planning work. Therefore, for effective implementation, the other medical officers should also assume responsibility for family planning work.

Relationship with Family Planning and M.C.H. Staff

Differences in the service conditions of the Family Planning and M.C.H. staff also appear to be creating a sense of discontentment among the staff, for instance, rent-free residential accommodation is provided to one category of workers in the Primary Health Centre and not to the others. Incentive money is paid to the Family Planning workers and not to M.C.H. workers. Attendant is provided to an Auxiliary Nurse Midwife under Family Planning and not to the ANM under M.C.H. The evaluation schedules for M.C.H. work and Family Planning are different and are separately maintained. These differences in their working conditions have adversely affected their relationships.[1]

Supervision

The annual budget report 1968-69 states that the Corporation is proposing to open 29 more new centres in urban areas with full-fledged staff required for all units. About 29 doctors, 50 extension educators, 8 lady health visitors or social workers, 58 ANMs, 29 compounders-cum-store keepers, drivers, one aya and 29 part-time sweepers, are sanctioned against these centres. The Primary Health Centres are also taking up the Family Planning activity.

The present survey shows that almost 50 per cent of the posts of Extension Educators were not filled. The present position is given in Table VI.2.

1. *The Report of the Working Group on Asian Population Studies on Administrative Aspect of Family Planning,* Geneva 1965, p. 20.

TABLE VI.2
Staff Position in Family Planning Section

Category of Staff	Sanctioned	In Position	Trained	Vacant
Doctors	42	32	30	10
Lady Health Visitors	15	10	8	5
Aux. Nurse Midwives	75	14	70	1
Extension Educators	55	29	25	35

The table indicates that except the Lady Health Visitors, the other staff fall short of the prescribed strength. This was mainly attributed to procedural difficulties, paucity of trained personnel and apathy of the administrators towards recruitment of the technical staff. There is a general tendency to take the staff from Central Health Department on deputation, rather than recruiting them directly.

The shortage of staff at supervisory as well as field level meant overwork and strain for them and had a telling effect on their efficiency. Continuous pressure for achieving the prescribed targets made them insensitive at times. In addition they were living under strenuous conditions. For instance, many of them had to travel as far as Kalkaji from Sadar Bazar and from Timarpur to Madangir, a distance of about twenty miles, in order to reach their place of work.

Procedural

Procedural delay in the release of funds and the problem of getting qualified persons for family planning work was mentioned to be the main reason for shortage of staff. But a scrutiny of the official files reveals that no effort was ever made to recruit the staff in a routine manner. Therefore, in order to expedite the recruitment, it was suggested that special powers should be given to the Deputy Director (M.C.H.) for recruiting the staff directly.

In a large-scale national programme like family planning detailed job description and work programme become an integral part of the staff planning. The role of various functionaries should be fully and precisely spelt out and overlaps eliminated. This can best be done by continuous appraisal of the work of the field staff. Furthermore, the Family Planning

Workers' manual prepared as early as 1964 needs to be revised and changed in the light of the experiences gained in the field over the years. It was also stressed that a long-range policy should be developed rather than effect frequent changes.

Effective administration of social services, among other things, depended considerably on the availability of timely supply of required inputs. The supply of inputs in case of family planning may be classified as (a) contraceptive materials, (b) clinical equipments, basic equipment for IUCD work and equipment for mobile unit, (c) administrative supplies, e.g., office equipments and forms etc. In a rural sub-centre, it was reported that sterilisation operation or IUCD insertion could not be performed due to absence of necessary accommodation. Sometimes mobile vehicles were the only venue for insertion of loop. It was mentioned that on several occasions the specific item required in the clinic was out of stock and also it took quite some time to indent it. For example, only big hospitals like Safdarjang and All India Medical Institute stocked oral contraceptives. It was difficult for the Corporation to avail it. In a programme like this long-term planning for effective supplies was necessary, taking into account local conditions of fund, distribution and communication system. In planning a programme for a particular unit, it is necessary to draw up a flow chart for supplies in order of their requirement. The aim of the programme should always be borne in mind to enable families to get contraceptives from traders or clinic sources.

Transport

Mobility of supervisory staff, service personnel and of supplies is essential for any programme. It was found that adequate number of vehicles were not available. For instance, van sanction for headquarters and the publicity van allotted for family planning work were out of order during the period of survey. It was attributed mainly to the lack of spare parts.

With extensive use of vehicles, it is unavoidable that a certain number will be temporarily out of order at any point of time. Therefore, a certain percentage of reserve fleet is required for emergency. The Administration while seeking budgetary provision should take this point into consideration. Secondly, the supervision on the use and handling of the vehicles, and maintenance of proper log book was considered necessary to ensure efficient functioning of vehicles. It may further be pointed out that special types of vehicles should be indented for rural areas and for audio-visual or mobile camps. Apart from these, the workers can be provided with cycles, scooters and scooter rickshaws for enhancing their mobility and thereby speeding up the work.

Budget

Provision of adequate funds is essential for any programme. Financial provision made at the Centre for Family Planning has to be transferred to the State authorities, who provide funds to the Corporation and voluntary organisations. One-twelfth of the annual allocation is available to Delhi Administration for each fiscal month for recurring expenses. Provision exists for purchasing supplies on a bulk basis. But the problem experienced by the Corporation appeared to be that of the time lag between the sanction of the budget and release of the grant. It was pointed out that the Corporation had to work for five months without any funds. On enquiry it was found that funds were not released to the health department in the absence of the audited reports. Sometimes review of their cases by the Delhi Administration protracted and delayed the release of funds. For example, it was reported during field survey that the Medical Officer could not disburse the incentive money to the motivators as there were not enough funds available. In the circumstances, inadequacy of funds during crucial period ultimately retards the programme.

This survey does not evidence any relaxation of bureaucratic procedure for release of funds for the special programme. Moreover, the officers responsible are constricted by rigid procedures followed for purchasing and for recruitment. It is, therefore, recommended that a balance between safeguards required for public finance and efficiency of operations may be reached.

Separate budget for Family Planning and M.C.H., as the former is sanctioned by the Centre and the latter is the responsibility of the Corporation, creates problem of relationship among the personnel. This duplicate source of financing creates a sense of compartmentalism among two categories of workers. M.C.H. staff suffers from inferiority complex because of inadequate financial provision at their disposal. On the contrary, it gave rise to a feeling of superiority among the Family Planning workers. Such feelings affected the relationship between two categories of staff.

In order to evoke a sense of participation among the local bodies, the Centre may work out a formula where the local bodies share the expenditure on the Family Planning programme. At present, it appears as if the centralised financial pattern of Family Planning has created a step-brotherly attitude towards the Family Planning programme. If finance permits, some contribution could at least be made to develop local initiative in planning the programme for the area. As far as possible, the budget of M.C.H. and Family Planning need to be amalgamated.

Evaluation and Record

Regular evaluation of the Family Planning work is a realistic tool for assessment of the progress of this programme. The Corporation Family Planning department has been using the prescribed proforma to assess the work of the centres.

During the survey, officials pointed out the problem arising out of the present reporting system. It was estimated by the National Institute of Health Administration and Education that 40 per cent of the time of the Auxiliary Nurse Midwife or Lady Health Visitor is spent on this work, while 25 per cent of their time is spent on travelling. Thus, they can only spend 35 per cent time on actual work. The Family Planning Case cards maintained for each family are compiled in the monthly progress reports which are submitted to the Central Office for recording purposes. Records, cards and registers for Family Planning and M.C.H. are maintained separately. This recording can help the administration to : (a) detect problems of implementation, (b) provide information needed for further planning, and (c) point to the gaps in action needed for further financial and other support. But how far these objects have been realised is a big question. The study of the files as

TABLE VI.3

Zone-wise allocation of budget in 1969-70 in Maternity Homes and Chief Welfare Centres, Municipal Corporation, Delhi

(Rupees in Lakhs)

Head of account	Head-quarters	City Zone	Shah-dara Zone	S.P. Zone	K. Bagh Zone	West Zone	Civil Lines	N.D. South Zone	Fateh-puri	Rural
Establishment	1.50	2.30	0.85	0.85	1.55	1.10	2.90	2.50	0.87	0.53
Contingency	0.45	.10	.03	.05	.05	.05	.10	.30	.05	.02
Medicine and Equipment	1.25	—	—	—	—	—	—	—	—	—
Stores	—	—	—	—	—	—	—	—	—	—
Diets	—	—	—	—	—	—	.05	—	—	—

Source : Corporation documents and files

well as information gathered from the interviews on decisional process revealed that no effort was made to utilize the information for that purpose. In this context it will be interesting to draw attention to the record of the Family Planning Centre of Basti Harphool Singh.

Year	Vasectomy	IUCD	Tubectomy	Total number of other methods & contraceptives
1964-65	Nil	Nil	Nil	4,734
1965-66	Nil	84	Nil	5,426
1966-67	4	170	Nil	5,846
1967-68	57	50	2	6,421
1968-69	68	10	2	7,521

The above information points to the irate and inconsistent development of the Family Planning Programme. Although there is constant increase in users of family planning practices, yet there is increase and decline in the number of persons using different methods. For instance, vasectomy cases were as high as 68 in five years but IUCD declined from 170 in 1966-67 to just 10 in 1968-69. Further, it is revealed that diaphragm, jelly, cantab and other traditional methods are more popular than new methods. It is also interesting to note that the Centre serves over 50,000 people of whom 70 per cent are Muslims. The fact that Muslims are taking to family planning practices in such a large number in one locality needs to be explored. A follow-up study of the Centre by the author revealed that while planning the programme for that particular Centre, the peculiar character of this area received no special attention. Neither of the Lady Doctors in charge of the Centre seems to have stressed on its peculiar characteristics. The usual target of IUCD is still imposed on this Centre for assessing the progress of the Centre. This clearly indicates that the time spent by the field staff in maintaining record is not well utilised for they are not put to best use.

In a family planning programme, it is essential for the planning administrator to know the impact of the programme in greater detail. It is, therefore, in the fitness of things that an evaluation cell staffed with a statistician, a medical officer and a health educator is appointed for the purpose. Also Central Family Planning Institute and Central Health Education Bureau may be requested to periodically provide their evaluation.

To ensure the accuracy of the monthly compilation work, the system of obtaining basic information should be simple and practical. While framing the proformas, it is necessary to ensure that the returns furnished can be easily verified. Secondly, the records must contain information on relevant indicators such as education, age, social position, earning etc. Thirdly, the recording system should not only show a tendency to overestimate the contribution of family planning programme to birth rate reduction, but the negative aspects of the programme must also be indicated.

Analysis of the statement showing progress of family planning in Delhi, appended to the report, reveals overall performance in case of percentage of target achieved. IUCD and sterilisation in 1967-68 was only about 431.8 in case of users of contraceptives against 195.3 per cent average achievement in Delhi. This clearly indicates that the Family Planning Units of the Corporation require administrative streamlining. However, the present Health Department has put up a comprehensive plan to develop the family welfare planning. Maternity and Child Health Section along with the hospital should serve a better strategy.[1]

Interrelationship with other Agencies

While reviewing the attitude of the voluntary organisations to health programme, most of the officials interviewed in Corporation Family Planning and Maternity and Child Welfare Centre expressed the view that the voluntary organisations are actually competing with the Corporation Centres. A visit to South Delhi rural colony revealed that the Lady Doctor of the Family Planning Centre, run by the Rotary Club, is not even aware of the existence of the Corporation Maternity and Child Health Centre, located a few yards away from it. It was point-

1. The recent strategy is to provide 15 bedded maternity home attached to each Maternity and Child Welfare Centre for integrated approach.

ed out that a strained relationship existed between the workers
of the voluntary organisations and that of the Corporation.

Besides local government, the voluntary organisations also
help in implementing the family planning programme. But it
has been generally observed that instead of pooling their resources and working in partnership they run counter and have
conflicts. The two have developed different styles and tradition and find it hard to establish functional relations. The
voluntary organisations are critical of the government for being
rigid, lacking innovation and, on the other hand, the voluntary
organisations are blamed for ignoring or even flouting rules. As
far as the voluntary organisations were concerned, there were
instances where they did not fulfil the minimum requirement.
Therefore, it is essential to arrange for proper supervision and
guidance of these agencies, so that they can execute the programme towards a desired goal. Whatever be their drawbacks,
it has to be recognised that voluntary organisations have a
positive role in the promotion of community service and hence
their contribution cannot be overlooked and undermined.

Family Planning and Private Practitioners

Lack of appreciation of the principle of community health
among private practitioners was further indicated by the workers
in the Family Planning programme. The Lady Health Visitors
reported cases where the women got the I.U.C.D. removed
by the private practitioners. It was reported that the private practitioners at times were apprehensive of the possibility
of developing cancer through loop insertion. It is difficult to
provide evidence to support it but it has been observed earlier
that the number of loop insertions has gone down considerably.

Corporation and other Agencies

In order to make family planning a success it is essential
that the government seek active support and cooperation of
its various wings engaged in community service and also that
of the voluntary organisations. Furthermore, it should use
mass media communication for educating people about the
need and practice of family planning.

Observations

It is evident from the foregoing discussions that administrative set up of the Family Planning Units is very much linked up with the Maternity and Child Health Centres, already organised on the traditional pattern. The Corporation Health Department aims to integrate the Family Planning activities with the existing M.C.H. Centres. However, this process of integration which ultimately has great bearing on the administrative efficiency of the programme, is still under experiment.

It has been revealed that the M.C.H. Centres have not been able to develop the services to cope with the needs of the growing population. This is more so in high concentration areas of Old City. There is hardly any centre in the areas which have newly sprung up. This has deprived these needy areas of family planning services.

The target fixed and administrative mechanisms devised will not succeed unless the staff members accept the programme and feel committed to its realisation. The staff members are to be trained and motivated for effective performance of their role.

The above discussion also indicates that the Family Planning Programme is not properly integrated with the health programme of the Corporation. Furthermore, no serious attempts are seemingly made for staff development and for motivating them to give their best performance. Thus, the programme implementation lacks both organisationally and in human motivation which are vital for its success.

CHAPTER VII

Personnel Management

Working of any organisational structure is to a considerable extent determined, among other things, by the quality of people and their work satisfaction. Therefore, Personnel Management acquires a great significance in the study of an organisation. This chapter attempts to examine the existing personnel policies. The term "Personnel Management" refers to a group of activities including recruitment of staff, placement, transfer, promotion, classification and pay, training, employees' health and welfare services, leave regulations, disciplinary action, retirement, supervision and delegation. It is used as a tool of management for the organisation.

Categories of Personnel

The medical and public health department is the most important branch of municipal service, employing the largest number of personnel (about 46.37%) in India. About 53 per cent of the total employees of the Corporation are engaged in the Health Department. The staff comprising 12,000 sweepers and 580 professionals in addition to other paramedicals can be categoried as shown in Table VII.1.

It may be noted that the Extension Educators and midwives sanctioned under planned programme are excluded

TABLE VII.1

Position of staff working in different categories in the Health Department as in July, 1969

Sl. No.	Categories of Staff	Sanctioned	On Roll	Quali-fied	Qualifications required
1	2	3	4	5	6
1.	Doctor (total)	334	307	280	Licentiate or MBBS with P.H. Diploma
	(a) Head Office Staff	22	22	18	M.D. or M.S. or MRCOG and P.H. Diploma
	(b) General Duty Officer	255	230	224	M.B.B.S.
	(c) Specialists	57	45	38	M.B.B.S. with post-graduate degree in respective field
2.	Nursing Staff (all levels)	470	400	400	Matriculate with train-ing in public health nursing/midwifery
3.	Administrative Officer	4	3	3	Graduation/ Interme-diate with experience in accounts and office work
4.	Accountants and Clerks	380	340	340	Intermediate/Matri-culate with typing and accounts knowledge
5.	Sanitarians	368	350	350	Matriculate with dip-loma in Health Sanitation
6.	Chemists	120	110	100	Higher Secondary with Organic Chemistry
7.	Technicians (X-Ray and Path. Lab.)	100	85	80	With diploma in Radiology or other specific subject con-cerned like Hospital Technicianship etc.
8.	Vaccinators	124	120	120	Matriculate
9.	Insect Collector and Rat Catcher	25	20	20	Class 8th standard with introduction to the subject
10.	Dispensers	106	60	60	Matriculate with dip-loma in Dispensing

1	2	3	4	5	6
11.	Sanitary Mate	134	130	120	Class 8th standard with recognised training in sanitarianship or matriculate with 5 years experience in the line
12.	Class IV employees	1,560	1,535	1,535	Class 8th standard and experience on subject
13.	Sweepers	12,000	11,800	11,800	Class IV standard education

This list includes Zonal Health Officer also.

here. Similarly, the Paediatrician and other staff in school health programme are excluded in the list as they are maintained under the Education Department ledger. As regards the number of the staff, the sweepers as a class predominates. About 184 'tractor drivers'[1] and 23 bullock cartmen are also included in the comprehensive list. It is worth noting that sweepers of different categories are employed in hospitals, dispensaries and maternity and child welfare centres. Among the professionals, next to the nursing staff comprising 838, come the sanitarians numbering 368, the single largest employees in one category. It is interesting to note that the department does not employ any psychiatric social worker in Silver Jubilee T.B. Hospital.

Pay Scales

We have already seen that the Health Department employs 15,000 persons. They are placed in different scales ranging from Rs. 70/- to Rs. 1,800/-. As per central government employees salary scale, Table VII.2 illustrates the seven categories of the staff employed in the department on the basis of their salary scale.

1. This term is used for describing the drivers of the vehicles of the Public Health Department.

TABLE VII.2

Pay scales of different categories of staff engaged in Health Department

Pay Scale	Categories of Staff	Total Staff
Rs. 1300-1600-1800	Municipal Health Officer	1
Rs. 1100-1300	Superintendent—Big Hosp.	2
Rs. 700-1300	Senior Specialists & Matrons	
Rs. 375-950	Junior Specialists & Matrons	81
Rs. 325-800 & 250-800	G.A.S. Grade I Doctors and other technical heads	128
	Sanitary Inspectors and Nursing Staff	
Rs. 130-300 & 110-180	Sanitarians, UDCs, Pharmacists, Dressers, Public Health Nurses etc.	368
Rs. 70-85	Sweepers and Class IV Staff	12,000

Of 580 technical staff, there are staff officers, Deputy Health Officers and Doctors in big hospitals in the grade of Rs. 700-1350. The Superintendents of the big hospitals enjoy almost the same salary as that of the Municipal Health Officer, Rs. 1150-1500 grade and Rs. 1300-1800 grade respectively. The Department also employs Doctors in Senior Specialist grade (Rs. 700-1250) and Junior Specialist grade (Rs. 375-950) and Civil Assistant Surgeon grade I Doctors in the scale of Rs. 325-800. These are comparable to the existing salary scales of the Central Government Health Service all over India.

The salary scales given above show that the Health Officer is in Super Time Grade II scale of the Central Government Health Service whereas the two Superintendents of the big hospitals are in a grade just below. The Senior Specialists, Junior Specialists are within Rs. 700-1300 scale, whereas the Matron, the head of the Nursing Service, is in Rs. 375-950 grade. The Matrons and Assistant Matrons are in the grade of Rs. 390-475 and Rs. 250-450. The Nursing Sisters, Head Clerks and Extension Educators are in Rs. 210-320 grade, whereas other technical staff are in Rs. 150-300 scale.

The non-medical administrative staff such as Upper Division Clerks and other technical paramedicals are in Rs. 130-300 grade while drivers, lower division clerks, public health nurses, dental hygienist, dispensers, dressers and other technical assistants are in the grade of Rs. 110-180.

Class IV employees, the sweepers, ayahs and cooks who predominate, being about 12,000 in number, are in the pay scale of Rs. 70-85.

As regards all these categories of personnel, the salary range of the services is almost comparable to other Government agencies in the metropolis. However, the salary scale of Civil Assistant Surgeons Grade I (Rs. 325-800) is lower than that of the Central Government Health Service (Rs. 350-900). But there again, these doctors are given special preference to join Central Government Health Service after working in municipal service for five years. It was mentioned that the Corporation was trying to recruit 75 per cent of the doctors from the Central Health Service and 25 per cent from the Corporation and to prescribe a uniform salary scales for Central Health Service and Municipal Medical Officers.

The staff in the Communicable Diseases Hospital and the T.B. Hospital are drawing similar scales of pay as doctors in other hospitals, whereas they are exposed to more hazards and infections.

Recruitment

Chapter VI, Section 89, lays down the recruitment policy of the Corporation. The Health Officer is one of the five principal officers of the Corporation. The rules and regulations of the Corporation personnel are also applicable to the employees engaged in the Health Department.

According to 1957 Act, the Commissioner is the key man in the personnel management system of the Corporation. The Corporation is empowered with the creation of all health posts with a minimum salary of Rs. 350/- and above. Appointments to all posts with a minimum salary of Rs. 350/- or more are vested in the Corporation. The Commissioner and the Standing Committee are delegated with power and authority for recruiting the personnel. In case of creation of all posts with salary less than Rs. 350/-, power is delegated to the Standing Committee. The Standing Committee can also create temporary posts for six months with a minimum salary of Rs. 3£0/- or more.

The Commissioner, on the other hand, is authorised to create temporary posts for six months carrying a salary less than Rs. 250/-. According to Section 96 of the Delhi Municipal Corporation Act, no post carrying minimum monthly salary of Rs. 350/- can be created without consultation with the Union Public Service Commission. No consultation is necessary in case of temporary posts for one year. If the post is created for more than one year in any case, it should not be extended beyond three years without consultation of the U.P.S.C.

However, in the case of almost all posts above a salary of Rs. 350/- per month, it is necessary to have consultation with the Union Public Service Commission for selection and recruitment of the candidates. In case of any difference of opinion between the Corporation authorities and the U.P.S.C., the matter is to be referred to the Home Department for final decision.

The qualifications for the staff to be employed have been laid down in consultation with professional bodies, such as the Indian Medical Association, Indian Nursing Council, Indian Dental Association.

Prevention of Food Adulteration Act 1954 prescribes that the Health Officer entrusted with authority to take legal action against violation of the Act must be a diploma holder in public health in addition to M.B.B.S. or licentiate qualification. Delhi Municipal Corporation Service Rule Regulation 5(3)11 are the rules operative for the sanctioning of leave for the Health Department employees. They are similar to the rules laid down by the Central Government.

As regards promotion, recruitment and job evaluation, the Corporation follows the Home Ministry Service Rules and it has no separate statute except the office memoranda issued from time to time. Corporation personnel policy is operative in the case of the Health Department. The Corporation Office Order Service Regulations 1959 framed by the Government of India under clauses (a) and (e) of sub-section (1) of Section 98, read with sub-section (1) of Section 480 of the 1957 Act and published by Ministry of Home Affairs Notification No.

40/11/58, Delhi dated 3rd April, 1959 in part IV, Delhi Gazette Extraordinary dated 4th April, 1959, page 80, are applicable to the personnel of the Health Department. FRs, SRs, CRs (Conduct Rules), etc., and instructions issued by Comptroller and Auditor General of India from time to time are applicable to municipal employees.

The study shows that about 90 per cent of the doctors in the department are recruited from the Health Ministry on deputation for varying periods of time. At present, they are trying to recruit 75 per cent from the Ministry and 25 per cent through open advertisement. About 80 per cent staff of the directly recruited cadre is kept on temporary basis. As regards staff in other categories, they are usually drawn from the general cadre of the Establishment and Administration Section. A Selection Board usually consists of the Health Officer, Deputy Commissioner for Health and Deputy Health Officer on the subject concerned. The selected persons are kept on a panel for appointment. The requisite number of candidates are further selected out of this panel. Eventually the Administrative Officer of the Health Department (as described in the previous chapter) with the consent of the Standing Committee through the Establishment Section issues the appointment letters to the selected candidates to join the service.

In case of a vacancy in a section, the official in charge is supposed to notify the Health Officer on the vacancy. He also sends the demand for the sanctioned post. It is then referred to the Administrative Officer, who, it has been observed, usually takes from four to five months to arrange for interview of the candidate. The selection is generally made from a list submitted by the Employment Exchange. Establishment Section arranges posting of the ministerial and clerical staff. As a rule 35 per cent of the posts are filled up by promotion from within. In case of the posts carrying higher salary scale than a basic of Rs. 350/-, the Commissioner acts as the Chairmain of the Selection Committee. It is then ratified by the U.P.S.C.

In actual practice, there are some deviations from the normal procedure of recruitment as discussed above. As we have already discussed, 1957 Act, Section 96, provides that as a special case, a suitable person can be appointed in a particular position for three years, beyond which the matter has to be notified to the Union Public Service Commission. But in practice, as was previously observed, about fifty per cent of the senior posts of the department are still kept temporary. The posts of the Deputy Health Officers were kept temporary as the Standing Committee could not decide upon regularising the posts. None of these posts have been referred to the U.P.S.C. The officials attributed this to the uncertainty about the flow of grant-in-aid from the Central Government. But some felt that it was a method of keeping the officials subservient to the politicians, who decide on the extension of their period of service.

In another case, it was reported that the establishment section manoeuvres cases to avoid the Union Public Service Commission for more than two years. It takes time to decide recruitment rule. Cases were reported where the U.P.S.C. was not consulted for over two years. The Standing Committee is yet to decide the recruitment policy in certain cases. Consequently, it was observed that most of the Zonal Health Officers were working on ad-hoc basis. Cases were also reported where Standing Committee had delayed its decision for over six years on the recruitment rules in regard to certain categories of personnel. In a particular case, it was observed that the Standing Committee was interested in recruiting persons but this could not be done. There was sharp difference of opinion between the U.P.S.C. and the Standing Committee on the selection of a particular candidate. The matter was then referred to the Home Ministry, which sent the verdict within a month. But the Standing Committee did not proceed with recruitment of anybody and the posts were still lying vacant for the last two years.

It was observed that an interesting way to avoid the U.P.S.C. (as usually practised by the Corporation) was to create lower grade posts (that is, carrying less than Rs. 350/-) and then upgrade them with the concurrence from the U.P.S.C.[1] This has resulted in the appointment of a large number of unqualified persons in different positions. During the period of study, it was evidenced from the records that about 300 to 350 officials were kept on ad-hoc basis in the Corporation. Out of these about 80 per cent were in Health Department. Two out

1. Statesman, January 19, 1970, p. 3.

of nine Zonal Health Officers were reported to be without any public health diploma, thus violating the Prevention of Adulteration Act 1954. The rules provide for filling in of 35 per cent of higher posts by internal promotion. But the official records indicate that no clear policy of internal promotion was being followed. The selection and promotion were largely ad-hoc and were made to suit the particular situation. There was a general feeling that recruitment was not always made on merit. Senior technical persons were quite diffident about the system for there was no scientific basis.

Table VII.1 shows that about 11 per cent sanctioned posts of Doctors have not been filled in. The paucity of staff was more marked in the case of Dispensers and the Nursing staff, where respectively 33 per cent and 14 per cent staff were not in position. When asked to state their difficulties in obtaining all these categories of staff, which were so vital for the running of the department, the Corporation authorities expressed their difficulties in securing suitable persons for medical services because of comparatively poor service conditions in the Corporation. Maximum difficulty was reported in securing trained nurses and dispensers.

Another problem was about the observance of the rules by staff. It was observed that the sweepers do not care for service rules and frequently remain absent. This creates problem for the recruitment of the staff.

It is interesting to note that about seventeen doctors, ten chemists and five technicians do not meet the minimum qualifications prescribed for the service. This sort of irregularity was attributed to pressures from the union for internal promotion. But the executives at the field level had other explanations to offer. According to them personal favour of the councillors has great influence in the placement practice of the Corporation.

One Upper Division Clerk of a particular section gave an interesting account of the way things happened in the Corporation. He was once interviewed for a post in higher scale. He was selected and kept in the panel. But the posts were not filled in for one year until the old list was scrapped.

On the other hand persons presumably known to the councillors were recruited from outside. Several such irregularities were pointed out but it is difficult to verify them. Such pulls and pressures, though occasional, provide scope for gossips and are very demoralising. It is evident that although the Corporation is a big employer yet it does not have any well worked-out personnel policies. This can be very damaging for the morale and efficiency of the employees.

It was revealed from the interviews that sometimes the executives avoided promotions to younger employees. This gave rise to frustration among the employees and also affected their efficiency and morale.

Supervision and Staff Development

The overall responsibilities of the local health personnel involve recording and analysis of health data for the purpose of planning and implementation of health services. The provision of direct environmental and personal health services (Medical Care), upkeep of the health facilities, coordination of activities and resources, supervision and regulation of all functionaries at the health department are the other responsibilities. Local health department has supervisory and regulatory functions covering various fields, such as protected water supply, food and milk supplies, control of nuisances, disposal of wastes, control of pollution and sources of infection, inspection of hospitals, dispensaries and school health programme.

In carrying out these functions the department uses various methods, the usual ones are official instructions through regulations, inspection, issue of licences and revocation of permits and legal measures. Supervision and inspection are also used as supportive services to the staff at lower levels so as to develop their skills and abilities. Right from the Municipal Health Officer, all other staff officials are responsible for supervisory functions at their respective levels. The study shows that right from the staff level officers such as Deputy Health Officer and the first line supervisors such as the Zonal Health Officers and the Inspectorate Staff are so much concerned with the official routine that they are not in a position to supervise even one-third of the institutions they are expected to.

The Deputy Health Officer in charge of the conservancy and public health is the most hard-pressed man in the matter. The responsibility of keeping the city clean from filth and dirt, and to arrange for the scavenging specially in the congested areas, rests with the Deputy Health Officer. He is practically in charge of all the sanitary staff in the city and the sanitary vehicles workshop.

He summons the meeting of the Zonal Health Officers once a week. He has to keep a record of the incidence of communicable diseases in the metropolis. Besides, he has to listen to the complaints and grievances of the ward councillors on sanitation of their areas. He has to attend the meetings of Health Committee. Sometimes, he is called to be in attendance when Corporation meetings take place. It was indicated that about 60 per cent of the time of the Municipal Health Officer and the Deputy Health Officer (Public Health) was spent in routine procedural work such as complying to the Councillors enquiries, answering queries like "Why such and such has been fined?", "Why there were no sweepers in a particular area?", "Why the wife of so and so sweeper was kept on duty beyond the prescribed hours?". Remaining 20 per cent of the time was given to the routine administrative matters. And 10 per cent was devoted to personnel problems like promotion, posting and group conflict etc. Thereby only 10 per cent of their time was left for area inspection and planning for future. It is thus evident that the staff members had very little time to attend to their duties.

Similar was the case with the Deputy Health Officer (Medical). He was not only responsible for the hospitals and dispensaries but also for the medical stores and equipments. Multifarious duties connected mainly with the stores and procurement and equipments left hardly any time for supervision. Consequently, it was found that there were some institutions which were inspected only once a year. Interestingly enough, a large number of these were located in the rural areas.

The Zonal Health Officer working as mini Municipal Health Officer is the coordinator for all medical and public health activities at the zonal level. Besides, he is in overall charge of the sanitary staff of the Corporation in his zone. Each zone employed over thousand sweepers. Visit to the Zonal Offices indicated that the Zonal Health Officers were very much concerned about the personnel problems related to the zones only.

The Health Officer also attended the Zonal Committee meetings as health expert. He had to attend to the grievances of the ward councillors. He had to go to the Town Hall once a week to meet the Deputy Health Officer (Public Health.) All these tasks took much of his time and he could not find time for supervising and inspecting the work of his subordinates in the area. A Zonal Health Officer once cynically remarked, "Though I am supposed to observe the water testing report daily but it is not possible for one to do so unless the waterborne disease actually assumes the proportions of an epidemic in the metropolis."

Besides, there were cases where heavy load of work was placed on certain staff members. For instance, in South Delhi Zone three Vaccination Inspectors were responsible for the area covering more than two lakhs of population, irrespective of the ecological character of the area. Jungpura, Bhogal, Nizamuddin, Sunder Nagar and Ashram areas were put under the charge of one official, whereas Mehrauli, Malviya Nagar, R.K. Puram, Motibagh and New Delhi South Extension Part II were under another official. One vaccinator is engaged to cover 45,000 people but in reality he cannot do that, consequently many areas were left uncovered for years together. It is thus evident that the work distribution of the staff was not made on a rational basis and the supervision also was rather poor and ineffective.

We shall now examine the workload for the doctors. Table VII.3 indicates the average workload of a doctor.

TABLE VII.3

Workload in Medical Relief for Corporation Staff (1969)

Institutions	No. of Doctors	No. of cases attended (old and new)	Attendance of cases per medical officer per day (average figure)
Allopathic Dispensary	62	27,32,907	121
Hospitals (Specialised and General)	131	22,05,121	46
Urban Health Centre	3	1,94,299*	177
Primary Health Centre	5	1,84,620*	151

* Indoor cases included.

Assuming that all the sanctioned posts are occupied, Table VII.3 is a pointer to the workload of cases per medical officer per day. It works out to as high as 177 cases in case of Urban Health Centre and the lowest is 46 in case of hospitals. It is to be remembered that these cases include all complicated indoor cases as well. Hospitals like I.D. and T.B. do not have any outdoor patient. Therefore, it is evident that workload figure in case of medical care is higher than that of C.H.S. dispensaries. It is evident that such a heavy case load leaves little time for the doctors to attend to other administrative work.

The foregoing discussion clearly suggests that the Medical Health Officer, the Deputy Health Officer, the Zonal Health Officer, the personnel on preventive side, the medical officers have little time at their disposal to fulfil their role as executives, supervisors, health planners, specialists and administrators. They only take up the activities which demand their immediate attention due to internal pressure; consequently more vital aspects of institutional management such as planning, coordination and staff development are ignored.

The supervisory role of an executive, in any institutional set up, can hardly be emphasized. This is more so in a setting where different skills and expertise are used for the treatment and cure of human beings. Several Commissions, Committees and Conferences have from time to time made observations on the personnel problems of the urban local bodies in India. For example, the Taxation Enquiry Commission (1953-54) spoke in favour of adequately paid and "well trained" municipal staff.

The Central Council of Local Self Government at its meetings in 1956, 1959 and 1960 and the Fourth Conference of Ministers of Town and Country Planning expressed concern over the efficiency and standard of municipal services and called upon the State Government to provincialise the administrative, health and other services of the municipalities. The latest recommendation is from Rural-Urban Relationship Committee which reported in 1967 among other things on municipal structure, personnel and finances. All these reports have made seething criticism of the existing personnel management of the country.

Punishment and Control

Section 480 of the 1957 Act dealing with disciplinary action against employees is also applicable to the staff working in the health department. The powers of reduction in salary, removal and dismissal from the post are vested with the appointing authority, that is, the Commissioner. This was needed in order to inject discipline in the organisation. As regards leave, transfer, suspension order and other disciplinary action the Central Government rules and regulations are operative.

The Fundamental Rules of the Government of India and Section 480 of the 1957 Act read with the Ministry of Home Affairs Notification No. 40/17/58, Delhi dated 3rd April, 1959, on page 77, Part IV, Delhi Gazette (extraordinary) dated April 4, 1959, are called the Delhi Municipal Corporation (Control and Appeal) Regulations, 1959. Section 7 of the notification suggests that the Disciplinary Authority shall frame definite charges on the basis of the allegations. Enquiry will be held on the allegations. Appeal can be made separately. The Standing Committee is empowered ultimately to take action against a defaulting official.

An important element in personnel management is supervision, control and punishment in deviant cases. Section 89 of the 1957 Act prescribes the measure of punishment. The Standing Committee can remove a person compulsorily asking to retire, being censured or for negligence of duty without serving any show cause notice (sub-section 3 of Section 89 of the Act). The study of Standing Committee minutes reveals that disciplinary action to the extent of dismissal was lodged against the medical officers for alleged dishonest practices. For example, in City Zone a doctor was dismissed for issuing licence to a bakery without taking fee. Deputy Health Officer (Malaria) was dismissed on the ground of showing 8,041 lbs. quinine consumed while it was not distributed. However, it is not always very easy to take disciplinary action against the defaulters, for officials in local bodies are able to muster the support of political leaders.

As a natural corollary to the present state of political enterprise, control and disciplinary action have become rather difficult in recent years. It is generally felt that power position has shifted from officials to political members. It was indicated that even transfer of a staff member from one station to another as a disciplinary measure may entail opposition from councillors, leave alone their dismissal or demotion. Administrators also feel that they are losing power for they find it difficult to enforce discipline at lower levels owing to unionisation. All this has detrimental effect on the morale of the people and inter-personnel relationships.

In the case of sweepers, who are indispensable for the nature of work they do, it is rather difficult to take disciplinary action. In their case, even for gross misconduct and absence from duty, the only punishment that can be inflicted is suspension.

As the appointing authority is the Commissioner, the right to appeal lies to the Council. On account of their size and composition, the Standing Committee and the Council are hardly suitable to act as appellate authorities. At times, they nominate someone as appellate authority. It is not surprising that officers and staff carry favour with the councillors for improving their prospects and saving them from the disciplinary action. It involves them in factional politics. Cases were reported of executive officers who are content with playing a subservient role, forsaking all drive and initiative in an anxiety to safeguard their position. Even where the subordinate staff is strictly under the control of an Executive Officer, the power of the Council to remove him limits his discretion in matters affecting control and supervision of his staff. Officials sometimes get identified with the groups in the Council and the subsequent changes in the composition of the Council following each general election affect their position. In this connection two instances were quoted wherein Executive Officers and other members of the staff were victimised by the new occupants in position.

Motivation and Morale

The study indicated that the staff were suffering from some sort of inferiority complex in having to work in the local body. They would prefer to have a position in Central or the State

Governments at the first opportunity, in spite of the fact that their salary was at par with that of Central Government.

As regards the attitude of the Executive to inspire and enthuse the juniors, it was difficult to draw any inference from this limited study. However, during the present study the author did not come across any concrete measure for motivating the juniors working in the field. Apparently, the monthly goal oriented meetings conducted by the Deputy Health Officer (M.C.W. & F.P.) with all her health visitors and family planning workers, were appreciated by the workers in the field. Officials felt that they can hardly find enough time to discuss with the juniors. Deputy Directors and the Health Officer are required to visit the zonal areas at least once a month, but they have not visited some areas even once during the last one year of this study. Consequently, conversation with the line officials in the field revealed that they do not have much communication with officials at the headquarters.

The communication process to inform the field workers about the latest policy and developments of the research finding on the subject have a useful impact on work and create motivation through personal relationship. The supervisors through personal contact can also foster psychological security. Absence of close communication, supervision and inspection has adverse repercussions on understanding of the functions they are meant to perform. It was reported that midwives in the Maternity and Child Welfare Centres still believed in 'counting of more heads" than actual practising of family planning devices.

So far as physical environment is concerned, the hospitals and the office accommodation appeared to be quite satisfactory. But offices were mostly housed in depressing and ill-ventilated rooms. The building which housed the Zonal Office in Karol Bagh was reported to be declared condemned about five years ago. The pathological laboratories were also usually located in such depressing environment, in the back door of the hospital.

With regard to working hours, most of the interviewees working in dispensaries had grievances. They felt that the timings of 8 a.m. to 12 p.m. and 6 p.m. to 8 p.m. were not quite suitable as it kept them engaged for the most part of the day.

The present working hours affected their personal as well as social life, as it gave them very little time for attending to their needs.

The Corporation, it is reported, has only the gratuity scheme in lieu of retirement pension for its employees. The staff transferred from Delhi Administration are entitled to pension benefit. But instances were observed where retired persons did not receive the benefit even after five years of their retirement. Interestingly enough there were cases where employees concerned died before they could receive the provident fund money. During the period of survey, the author met two eminent retired doctors, who narrated their experience of harassment in availing pension benefit, as their service was transferred from Delhi Administration to the Corporation in 1958. If this is the case with professionals, the plight of office staff would surely be worse.

The professionals like doctors and paramedicals are required to make several trips all over their working areas and they are entitled to conveyance charges. But the discussion with the Administrative Officer (Head Office) revealed that the procedure of reimbursement of the amount is so cumbersome that the professionals would rather go without it. This may as well be the reason behind the inertia of the personnel to move out of their office to carry out inspection work. The Corporation authorities would do well to improve and simplify reimbursement procedures so as to overcome the inertia or as an alternative, the staff may be paid a fixed sum as conveyance allowance.

The staff of the Corporation are entitled to free medical benefits. But how many of them really avail of these benefits? The study shows that quite a large percentage go to the private practitioners as they have no faith in the medicines given at the Corporation dispensaries. The Corporation Personnel Department is supposed to look after the welfare of the Corporation employees. A limited number of family and child welfare centres are being run as a part of welfare measures. There are three Welfare Officers to look after the welfare activities meant to cater to 38,000 workers of the Corporation. This number is surely inadequate and it is also essential that there should be trained social workers in the personnel department for systematically organising social welfare programmes based on the needs of the employees.

Job Unrelated to Salary

An analysis of the categories of staff given in Table VII.1, shows that the pay structure is not related to job requirements. The same range of duties or the equal degree of responsibility are not assigned to similar grades. The remuneration is not commensurate either with position or with the nature of the job. For instance, the Workshop Engineer (in charge of the Workshop) is supervised by the Deputy Health Officer (Public Health) and both are placed in the same grade of Rs. 700-1100. The pay scale of the Zonal Health Officer, supervising also the activities of the local hospitals, is at par with that of the Resident Superintendent of any hospital, e.g., Rs. 450/- basic pay.

The Dispensers while doing technical job like Laboratory Technician are in different grades, viz., Rs. 130-240 and 160-330 respectively. The Dressers are in the scale of Rs. 80-110, a little above ward boys and cooks getting Rs. 75-95.

In the case of the class IV staff, the salaries of Sweepers and Peons are comparable, whereas the Sweeper's job is more menial and strenuous. However, the health bye-laws provide special service facilities like arrangement of quarter for the Sweeper.

The staff in the Communicable Diseases Hospital and the T.B. Hospital are drawing the same scales of pay as doctors of other hospitals, whereas the former are exposed to greater hazards. Only 25 per cent of this category of staff are provided with residential quarters.

The 'motivation' of personnel administration is significantly related to the efficient working of the personnel management. These broad areas are primarily the responsibility of departmental management. But the establishment section has its own responsibility for two kinds of activities, viz., (i) dissemination and interpretation of research findings and (ii) administration of service-wise programme established by the management for improving motivation, discipline and employee morale. There is need to have a personnel policy focussing the emotional and environmental needs of the staff.

Closely related to motivation is the employee morale, the essential ingredient for the efficient operation of any personnel policy. It is difficult to define the term 'morale'. The behaviouristic school has placed more emphasis on good leadership, job and employee training to develop proper attitude towards his activities. If the employee is expected to give his best to his job, it should in turn give him the satisfaction. The work must give him sense of self-realisation and fulfilment on the one hand and opportunities for growth and development on the other.

Employer-Employee Relations

This is the most significant aspect of personnel management. There has been a steady increase in unionization all over the world. A similar trend is observed in Corporation health employees too. In earlier periods, professionals like doctors and nurses usually kept out of this. But the incidence of strike among the junior medical practitioners in the Corporation following the strike in Central Government hospitals in early 1969 and nurses' strike in 1968 and the nurses' strike in Victoria Zanana Hospital in 1967, and the frequent strikes of class IV employees in T.B. Hospital are indications of Union activities in recent years. Pointing to the strikes a union leader of hospitals said, "Strike is the only language that the authorities understand." During the period of study the sweepers of the entire Corporation area and sweepers of the South Delhi Zone went on strike twice to protest against their poor working conditions. This is indicative of the growing dissatisfaction among the employees. Nothing can be said with exactitude as to what are the reasons behind it. This in itself can be an interesting area of enquiry.

However, the Hospital Review Committee (1969) attributed the current deterioration in law and order situation in the municipal hospitals to strong trade unionism among hospital employees.

The author interviewed 20 sweepers out of 40 who squatted before the New Delhi Municipal South Zone Office. Some of their grievances are listed below :

1. Absence of staff quarters for the municipal employees in general and those having emergency duties in particular. The Corporation bye-law contains provision for residential accommodation for the sweepers but in effect a large percentage are without accommodation.
2. Absence of any duty roster for class IV employees. They do not have any job chart of their duties.
3. Absence of provident fund benefit for class IV staff.
4. Misplacement of personal files of the sweepers.
5. Delay in fulfilling the promises made earlier by the authorities.

Some of the observations above were found valid during the period of study. Duty roster is not maintained in proper order. It was not kept uptodate. It was admitted by the officials that the personal files of class IV employees were not properly maintained. Some expressed doubts if they were maintained at all. Absence of staff quarters for class IV employees and Sweepers became evident during the field visit of the author. At one time the strike of the class IV staff continued for over one month. The health executives became very nervous about the matter. The Zonal Assistant Commissioner referred the case to the Corporation. The Corporation Commissioner, however, granted them interview and promised to take up the matter with the Home Ministry. The strike was withdrawn on the assurance from the Commissioner that the Corporation would earnestly try to redress their grievances. Neither the Health Officer nor the Commissioner has much to do in some of these matters. However, they can very well insist on having a better personnel agency of the Corporation to look into the welfare of the staff.

All these findings seem to suggest that little attempts have been made to devise personnel policies, conducive to welfare of the employees on the one hand and harmonious relationship between the employers and the employees on the other. There is hardly any programme for staff development.

It is, therefore, essential that the Municipal Corporation employing such a large manpower should develop effective personnel agency with well defined policies and programmes for the betterment and welfare of the staff. Such a policy and programme will undoubtedly go a long way in fostering better relationship between the employers and the employees.

CHAPTER VIII

Financial Management

Financial management is a significant aspect of any administrative system, for it calls for maximum utilization of scant resources. Management of financial resources becomes all the more important in the context of underdeveloped economy, for welfare of the people is to be achieved under great financial constraints.

The purposes of financial management are : (a) to ensure that expenditures are made legally and within the availability of funds, (b) to provide current and specific information to the management, (c) to make effective expenditure through proper budgeting and purchasing.

In financial management, we are mostly concerned here with its application as a tool for making intelligent allocation of resources keeping in view the goals and the available resources. We shall examine how the financial management of the health department takes place in the framework of the Corporation.

Legal Provision

At the outset it may be useful to enumerate the existing legal provision regarding financial management. The rules and regulations with regard to budget formulation of the Corporation are laid down under the Corporation Act of 1957.

Trend Of Percentage Of Expenditure On Health Department Of Delhi Municipal Corporation During 1958-70

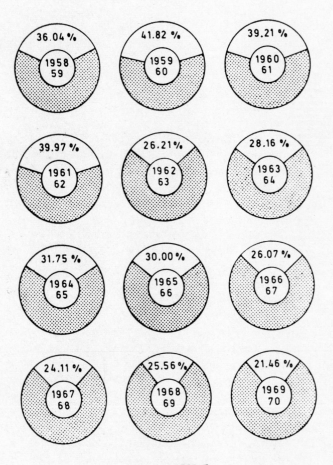

Fig. **VIII.I**

The budget estimate is to be prepared in a form "as may be appropriated by the Standing Committee and presented and adopted in such manner and shall provide for all matters, as are prescribed by regulations made in this behalf." The Commissioner in consultation with the departmental heads formulates the budget for a fiscal year. In this process of budget formulation, the departmental heads are responsible for developing plans, policies and recommendations for the coming financial year. The Standing Committee is the scrutinising authority of the draft budget proposals of the Commissioner. The budget as decided by the Standing Committee has to be placed before the Corporation Council for their approval.

Corporation Finances

Before we discuss the existing practices of budget formulation in the health department, it may be logical here to discuss the financial position of the Corporation as a whole. The budget of the Corporation is an estimate of its expenditure in the background of its income. Therefore, we may first of all consider the sources of income of the Corporation, of which health department is one of the recipients. The Corporation derives income from the following sources :

(a) Domestic sources of revenue : (i) Revenues raised from the Corporation taxes as levied by the Corporation Act and (ii) fees, fines and other receipts.

(b) External sources : (i) Share of Central taxes assigned to the Corporation and (ii) grants-in-aid from the Government.

In the financial year 1966-67, as the annual reports indicate only 44% of the revenue of the Corporation was raised from the domestic sources and the remaining 56 per cent from the share of assigned taxes and government grants.

A brief review of the financial position of the Corporation suggests that during 1958-61, the Corporation received grants-in-aid to the extent of 50 lakhs on the schematic budget on ad-hoc basis. In case of grants-in-aid no definite pattern seemed to have been followed. It usually changes from year to year.

Consequently, no scheme could be formulated as a phased programme. Apparently, this practice leaves the functional departments in a state of insecurity. The elaborate financial rules of the Central Government have also a restrictive tendency, hampering a wide range of activities.

The Corporation receives grants and subsidies from the Centre only to meet the incurred expenditure. But the amount is released only at the end of the financial year. The Corporation therefore finds it difficult to make current payments as there is a vast gap between the receipt and the payment.

With regard to internal resources of all the big Corporations in India, Delhi has the lowest percentage of income from taxes.

The Corporation, which was running a deficit of about Rs. 160 lakhs, had developed some liabilities. As already indicated, Delhi as a metropolitan city has a comprehensive urban development plan, with metropolitan and regional complexes. The Corporation is expected to provide essential services in the developed areas under the Master Plan of Delhi. All these entail heavy expenditure on development of colonies and specially that of rural areas; however, the costs of personnel administration being at par with Central Government, the rise in salaries, increase in maintenance expenditure on planned schemes without corresponding rise in revenues put a heavy strain on the budget of the Corporation leading to deficit financing. The finances are required for social and economic development of the Corporation. Therefore, it was quite logical for the Morarka Commission to recommend a systematic process of collection of revenue to strengthen the internal resources of the Corporation. This will definitely result in systematic execution of the services programme of the Corporation.

Expenditure

Of all the Corporations in India, maximum per capita expenditure is made in Delhi, in contrast to Trivandrum which spends the minimum amount. Public health, the most important service of an urban local body, accounts for Rs. 20.50 per capita in Delhi Corporation and only Rs. 3.65 per capita in the case of Hyderabad indicating the ratio of 1 : 7 between the maximum and minimum level of services. Education, the next major important service, accounts for Rs. 3.45 for all the Corporations. Among individual Corporations it varies from Rs. 8.80 in Delhi to Rs. 0.66 in Bangalore.

Expenditure on public works is the highest, accounting for over one-third of the total expenditure. Public health ranks second, whereas education, general administration and public safety are other significant single items.

On an analysis of the pattern of revenue and expenditure of the Delhi Corporation, it was found that a large part of the Corporation expenditure is incurred on the pay and allowances and service establishment like sweepers, doctors in health and teachers in education department. The percentage of expenditure incurred on establishment of the Corporation is indicated in Table VIII.1

TABLE VIII.1

Trends in Expenditure on Establishment

Item	1961-62	1962-63	1963-64	1964-65	1965-66	1966-67	1967-68
Percentage of expenditure on service establishment	84.3	84.8	84.9	84.0	85.3	88.7	88.9
Percentage of expenditure on supervisory establishment	9.5	9.8	9.5	10.1	9.0	7.0	6.8

Table VIII.1 indicates steady rise in cost of establishment from 84 per cent to 89 per cent, whereas the expenditure on supervisory services is on the decrease, from 9.5 per cent to 6.8 per cent during the period 1961 to 1968. This leaves only 3 per cent of the total amount to be spent on actual services.

Table VIII.2 is an attempt to indicate the expenditure pattern of the Corporation on Medical and Public Health in relation to other departments.

TABLE VIII.2

Percentage of Expenditure under Water Supply and other heads of the Health Department

Year	General Supervision and tax collection	Water Supply	Public Health	Medical Relief	Conservancy & street cleansing	Scavenging of drains etc.
1958-59	9.44	14.59	4.68	8.57	11.46	11.33
1959-60	5.05	7.56	5.32	10.66	12.46	13.38
1960-61	4.11	5.71	5.40	9.77	11.13	12.91
1961-62	5.49	5.32	5.20	9.59	12.16	13.02
1962-63	5.77	1.84	5.27	9.08	12.36	9.00
1963-64	6.74	2.20	5.05	9.60	12.13	1.38
1964-65	5.89	0.79	4.20	8.32	12.02	7.20
1965-66	6.17	1.63	4.33	9.69	12.93	3.05
1966-67	2.88	4.71	3.55	10.13	11.89	0.50
1967-68	4.41	8.80	3.32	9.93	10.43	0.45
1968-69	4.16	0.57	2.80	9.06	9.27	0.43
1969-70	3.83	11.68	2.76	9.21	9.49	0.43

Source : Municipal Corporation Year Book 1970, p. 59

This table points out the significant decline in percentage expenditure on public health and conservancy, drastic reduction in scavenging of drains from 11.33% to 0.43% and a slight rise in medical relief from 8.57 per cent to 9.21 per cent during the last ten years. Although the total amount spent on each item is on the increase, the percentage of total expenditure of the Corporation is on the decline.

Table VIII.3 indicates that the expenditure on public health and medical relief has remained almost steady with minor variations. The highest amount as a single major item is spent on education. The expenditure on public health and medical services has remained almost steady whereas a significant fall in the scavenging is indicated. Conservancy and street cleansing unit have almost similar percentage of expenditure with minor variations.

Fall in expenditure on scavenging is attributed to the change in the procedure of account keeping, as the repair of drains has been transferred to the head of account of Public Health and Engineering. However, the data indicate that the

TABLE VIII.3

Expenditure on Health Services in relation to other Social Services of the Corporation

Item	1965-66		1966-67		1967-68		1968-69	
	actuals	%	actuals	%	actuals	%	actuals	%
General Supervision	69,39,291	9.6	41,26,380	4.5	67,94,766	6.5	97,42,400	9.7
Education	2,66,95,275	36.9	4,70,28,081	51.5	5,14,72,443	49.6	3,36,70,000	33.5
Public Health	48,71,756	6.7	50,79,511	5.5	59,00,514	5.7	6,37,05,000	6.3
Medical Relief	1,08,98,198	15.1	1,44,92,544	15.9	1,68,91,396	16.3	2,05,64,000	20.5
Conservancy and street cleansing	1,45,39,123	20.1	1,70,19,357	18.6	1,88,70,226	18.3	2,06,50,300	20.6
Scavenging drains and sewers	34,28,556	5.8	7,13,594	0.8	8,55,506	0.7	9,01,400	0.9
Slum clearance	49,05,450	6.8	29,01,275	3.2	30,03,988	2.9	85,24,900	8.5

Medical and Public Health Department jointly spent the largest percentage of revenue from the amount apportioned for social services during the years 1965 to 1969.

Expenditure on Health Department

It may be useful at this point to indicate that the Health Department expenditure is incurred under the following heads :

(a) Medical Care,
(b) Public Health,
(c) Conservancy,
(d) Scavenging.

Table VIII.4 indicates a trend of increase in expenditure on health services from Rs. 1.64 crores to Rs. 4.73 crores during the period 1958-59 to 1966-67. It is highly significant in the case of Medical Care and Conservancy, where it has risen from 0.39 crore to Rs. 1.68 crores and from Rs. 0.52 crore to Rs. 1.70 crores respectively. The expenditure percentage on scavenging and drains is almost constant, although it had a leap in 1965-66 to 2.38, and again declined to 0.85 crore in 1967-68. This is highly significant in the background of population explosion in the metropolis and expansion of colonies.

From the general phenomenon of the allocation of resources to Health Department, we may proceed to analyse the amount spent on the establishment of each unit of the Health Department. This will further indicate the major items of expenditure of the Health Department.

Medical Care

Allocation of budget on medical care is classified under the following four heads :

(a) General Establishment,
(b) Hospitals, Clinics, Maternity and Child Welfare Centres,
(c) Dispensaries,
(d) Family Planning Centres.

Break Up Of Expenditure Health Department

(Rupees In Crores)

Fig. VIII.2

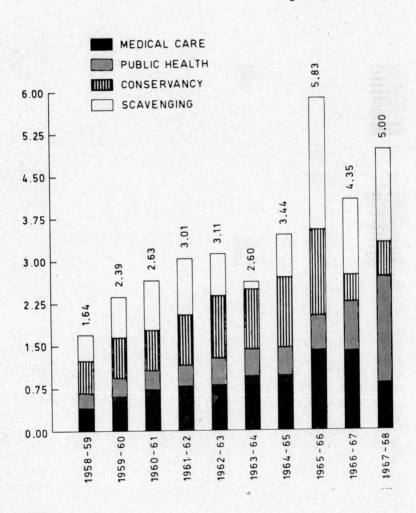

TABLE VIII.4
Break up of Expenditure on the Health Department (in crores)*

Section	1958-59	1959-60	1960-61	1961-62	1962-63	1963-64	1964-65	1965-66	1966-67	1967-68
Medical Care	0.39	0.61	0.66	0.62	0.79	0.89	0.90	1.35	1.44	1.68
Public Health	0.21	0.31	0.36	0.39	0.46	0.46	0.46	0.54	0.50	0.59
Anti-Malaria, Maternity & Smallpox etc.										
Conservancy, street cleansing & Road watering	0.52	0.71	0.75	0.92	1.08	1.12	1.30	1.55	1.70	1.88
Scavenging	0.52	0.77	0.86	0.98	0.78	0.13	0.78	2.38	0.71	0.85
Drains & Sewers										
Grand Total	1.64	2.39	2.63	3.01	3.11	2.60	3.44	5.83	4.35	5.00

* Family Planning is not included here.

TABLE VIII.5

Break up of Expenditure on Medical Care

Item	1966-67		1967-68		1968-1969	
	actuals	%	actuals	%	actuals	%
General Establish-ment	3,51,462	2.5	8,54,109	5.1	26,85,700	13 4
Hospitals, Clinics, MCW Centres	1,13,11,562	80.1	1,28,41,898	77.4	1,39,40,100	69.6
Dispensaries : Allopathic, Homeo-pathic & V.D. Clinics	24,53,638	17.4	27,46,769	16.6	33,16,000	16.7
Family Planning Centres*			1,51,374	0.9	71,000	0.3
Grant Total	1,41,16,662		1,65,94,150		2,00,12,800	

* This has been dealt with separately under the Chapter on Family Plan-ning.

Table VIII.5 indicates that while expenditure on general establishment of the medical care services was on the increase during the last three consecutive years from 2.5 per cent to 13.4 per cent, the allocation on hospitals and dispensaries was on the decline. Allocation on the dispensaries was somewhat steady.

While dispensaries have increased in number during recent years, it was difficult to obtain correct information about the allocation of budget on Family Planning Centres, as the amount is mostly dependent on Central Government grant. The amount shown is the proportion spent from the Corporation budget.

Table VIII.6 indicates the break-up of expenditure on big hospitals. It is evident that establishment accounts for a large chunk of the expenditure. Assuming that in a social service agency balanced allocation of resources is essential to obtain optimum result, the study of these big hospitals and the T.B. hospitals shows that the highest percentage of the budget is spent on establishment whereas the amount spent on diet, equipments and stores is insignificant. The budget estimate of the department's smaller hospitals in the different colonies however indicates that 67 per cent of the total outlay is spent on establishment, while only 15 per cent is spent on medicine.

TABLE VIII.6

Statement of expenditure on various items in big hospitals, M.C.D. (1968-69)

Big Hospitals	Estt.	Contingency	Equipments & Apparatus	Diet	Stores	Upkeep of Bldgs.	Medicine & Instrument	Budget Estts.
H.R. Hospitals	14.60	1.50	1.50	0.75	1.00	0.22	5.50	26.87
S.J.T.B. Hospital	17.45	1.20	0.60	9.30	1.00	0.070	4.00	33.88
V.Z. Hospital	8.575	0.90	0.50	0.65	0.50	0.097	1.30	12.52
B.R. Hospital	0.85	0.10	0.005	0.11	0.01	0.031	0.30	1.43
C.H. Shahdara	0.87	0.06	0.01	0.025	0.25	—	0.45	1.44
I.D. Hospital	4.997	0.30	0.10	0.50	0.10	0.043	1.00	7.04
G.L. Mty. Hospital	3.20	0.40	0.15	0.20	0.20	—	0.50	4.65
G.H. Shahdara	4.80	0.38	0.25	0.15	0.15	—	1.75	7.48

However, the trend of expenditure on medical services suggests top heavy nature of the Corporation medical care services. The heavy burden on establishment leaves very little share of revenue for actual services.

It is worth examining whether such a large part of the budget should be spent on salaries of the staff for health services. With such an imbalance in budget allocations, one wonders whether the Corporation can maintain the required standard of service. Commenting on this point a senior officer pointed out, "Sometimes I wonder whether the Corporation could afford this luxury of providing medical care services to the metropolis with such limited resources, which are hardly enough for concerted effort on public health side." Is it more for political than real cause that the Corporation is spending on medical relief?

Public Health

The allocation of resources for public health is also made under five heads, e.g., (i) establishment, (ii) epidemics, (iii) vaccination, (iv) malaria & insecticide and (v) miscellaneous like monkey catch, cremation ground, statistics, etc. Table VIII.7 indicates the relative importance given to different items of services on the basis of allocation of funds under each head during 1966-67 to 1968-69.

It suggests that there is decline in expenditure on public health items almost by half and there is steady rise in expenditure on establishment from 22.1 per cent to 37.5 per cent. While the amount on malaria control has doubled, the percentage on miscellaneous items and vital statistics has declined by half. Likewise allocation on epidemics is somewhat constant while it has increased on immunization programme. Although the percentage of budget expenditure on establishment is lower in the case of public health than on medical care, it is brought out that major part of the total budget allocation is spent on establishment, which can only justify its existence through proportional balanced expenditure on other items. In the background of the scarcity of resources of the Corporation, it is necessary to examine critically the benefit

TABLE VIII.7
Break-up of expenditure on Public Health

Items	1966-67 actuals	%	1967-68 actuals	%	1968-69 actuals	%
Establishment	20,25,905	22.1	21,43,028	38.3	21,28,000	37.5
Epidemics	4,99,076	5.5	4,24,696	7.6	3,92,500	6.9
Vaccination	4,19,953	4.6	4,69,919	8.4	4,79,000	8.5
Malaria & Insecticide	11,29,017	12.3	14,21,766	25.4	14,12,000	24.9
Miscellaneous : Monkey catch, cremation grounds, statistics etc.	50,79,511	55.5	11,35,380	20.3	12,56,000	22.2
Grand Total	91,53,462		55,92,889		56,67,500	

derived from the administrative expenditure incurred on top heavy administration.

Present Procedure of Budget Formulation in Health Department

As indicated earlier, the Heath Officer is primarily responsible for submitting the annual budget proposals to the Commissioner on the basis of the approved policy. Observation and discussion with the staff reveal that the Zonal Health Officers are asked to provide a financial layout on the basis of the expenditure pattern of the previous year.

As the expenditure pattern is mainly determined by the salary and the establishment expenditure on different units, the budget is based on those very items. The Zonal Health Officer thereafter submits the budget proposals to the Deputy Health Officer on different heads. The Deputy Health Officer then prepares the annual budget estimate on the basis of these reports. The budget estimates prepared by the different heads of the units are coordinated by the Accounts Section of the Corporation. Ultimately the budget report is prepared and placed before the Standing Committee by the Commissioner. During this process a great deal of reduction takes place. Finally, the Corporation ratifies the budget proposals in March.

The study, therefore, reveals that the budget is framed on the basis of the previous year's estimated expenditure on manpower rather than on the "consumers' need". In actual practice, there should be a periodic assessment of the health needs of the population. An objective and systematic indicator of per capita health should be developed by the research organisation. It would be most appropriate to have a rational and systematic basis for budget formulation.

The Health Officer is an innovator to develop the proposals which would improve the health services for the citizen in the metropolis. It should be then up to the Commissioner through the Deputy Commissioner to determine the acceptable proposals. Since the latter is not a professional in the field it is safer to assume that the Health Officer is an innovator and the Commissioner is the selector.

Problems

Apart from the meagre resources and the allocation of resources for various heads on the basis of Corporation policy, the related problems of financial management of the Health Department have been classified and discussed in the following paragraphs.

Voluntary Organisations

Voluntary grants-in-aid may be made by the Corporation at their discretion to associations or institutions carrying out any obligatory or discretionary duties of the Corporation, as laid down in the Corporation Act 1957.

The Corporation spends about Rs. 10 lakhs as grants-in-aid to various welfare organisations every year. About 70 per cent of this amount is spent on dispensaries and hospitals run by the voluntary agencies. The amount sanctioned to an institution depends on the financial position and the needs of the institution. It varies from Rs. 5,000 to Rs. 10,000 per year.

Rules of Payment of Grants-in-aid

The following conditions are prescribed by the Municipal Corporation of Delhi for the purpose of giving voluntary grants-in-aid to institutions in Delhi, other than those receiving grants-in-aid for education from the provision therefor in the Corporation's budget.

1. Voluntary grants-in-aid are given to the institutions with the aims and objects as given below :

(a) To promote adult literacy.

(b) To promote care or education of the deaf, the dumb, the mute, the blind and the crippled and handicapped.

(c) To promote, establish and run poor houses, infirmaries, children's homes, orphanages, homes for deserted women and shelters for destitutes.

(d) To promote, establish and run museums, art galleries, reading rooms and libraries.

(e) To promote sports and games and establish and run stadia, gymnasia and akharas.

(f) To promote, establish and run social service centres, work centres and women's social and educational activities.

(g) To promote, establish and run health centres, hospitals, dispensaries, maternity homes, leper homes and lunatic asylums.

(h) To promote care of and relief to beggars, moral rehabilitation of women and delinquents.

(i) To provide benefits and benevolence of any kind falling under clause (za) of Section 43 of Delhi Municipal Act.

2. No grants will be made if the association or institution is not conducted for any charitable or benevolent purposes.

3. The grants made by the Corporation will be restricted to such activities as are carried on within the limits of Delhi.

4. No grant will be made, if in the discretion of the Corporation, it is found that the amenities provided or the services rendered by a particular association or institution are not necessary in the particular locality in which they are provided.

5. No grant will be paid to any institution or association in which religion is a condition of admission or if its activities include propaganda for conversion of faith or religion.

6. Grants will be made subject to the following considerations :

(i) If an association or institution requires a capital grant for its activities or an extension thereof, assistance may be given by the Corporation at their discretion if such association/institution is registered under the Societies Registration Act (Act XXI of 1860). The grant will be for such amount as the Corporation may fix having regard to the financial position of the association or institution and the object for which it is needed.

(ii) An annual grant towards meeting the current expenses of an association or institution may be given subject to the following :

(a) No grant will be given in cases in which fees, other than nominal fees in the opinion of the Corporation, are charged for the benefits, amenities or services provided.

(b) No grant will be given in the case of an association or institution, the balance sheet of which for each of the three preceding years shows a surplus exceeding the amount of the grant-in-aid paid by the Corporation during each of these years.

(c) No grant will be given if it is found that the activities are not carried on properly and economically or that funds are either not utilized for which they are intended, or are mismanaged.

(d) No grant will be given to an association or institution which is not open to all classes and communities.

(e) No grant will be made if the amenities or services are rendered to a class of people, who can themselves afford to pay for such amenities or services.

(f) Concession in rent, taxes, etc., already made by the Corporation will be taken into account in fixing the amount of the grant.

7. Each association or institution applying for a grant must have a regular constitution of its own specifying its aims and objects and rules and regulations for the conduct of its affairs.

8. An institution or association applying for a grant for the first time or in subsequent years shall submit its application to the Commissioner not later than the 30th June, each year.

9. (a) Every application must contain the following information :

(i) Name and address.

(ii) Aims and objects.

(iii) Composition of the Board of Management.

(iv) Copy of the Annual Report for the immediately preceding year.

(v) Statement showing the income, expenditure, resulting surplus or deficit, the grant received from the Corporation (or its predecessors) or Government and the concessions in rent, taxes, etc. granted by the Corporation (or its predecessors) for the immediately preceding three financial years.

(vi) Balance sheets for the immediately preceding three financial years.

(vii) The fees, subscriptions etc. charged from the public or members for taking the benefit of the association or institution.

(viii) Copy of registration certificate.

(b) In the case of new institutions applying for a grant for the first time, the requirements under (v) and (vi) above may, where inevitable, be confined to the immediately preceding year only.

10. The Commissioner shall scrutinise the applications received and as soon as possible and in any case, not later than the 31st August, put up before the Corporation through the Grants-in-aid Committee a tabular statement giving briefly the particulars mentioned at (a) and (b), and his recommendations in respect of each institution.

11. The Corporation shall consider and pass orders on the Commissioner's proposal as soon as possible and in any case,

not later than the 15th of October.

12. The grants decided upon shall be disbursed within 15 days of the date of resolution of the Corporation.

13. Nothing in paras 9 to 12 shall preclude the Corporation, in exceptional cases, from considering and passing orders on requests for the payment of grant in advance, monthly or quarterly from associations or institutions, which would otherwise be seriously handicapped in carrying on their activities. Applications with such requests should be made, with all the particulars specified in para 7, by the 30th April of a year, and must explain the reasons for which an exception to the annual basis of payment of grants is desired. The Commissioner will submit such applications to the Corporation through the Grants-in-aid Committee by the 31st May, at the latest.

14. An institution to which a grant is sanctioned must agree to the following :

(a) The inclusion of one representative of the Corporation on its Board of Management if the amount of grant is upto Rs. 1,000 and two or more representatives of the Corporation on its Board of Management if the amount of grant exceeds Rs. 1,000.

(b) The submission for the information of the Corporation of the annual report and audited balance sheet for the previous year certified by a recognised auditor or a firm of recognised auditors, but in the case of small institutions receiving a grant-in-aid not exceeding Rs. 500 per annum, the audit of accounts by recognised auditors will not be insisted upon.

(c) Allow inspection of accounts and documents whenever required by the said representatives of the Corporation.

15. A grant shall be subject to reconsideration every year.

16. The representative of the Corporation on the Board of Management of an association or institution to which grants are given shall submit to the Corporation their reports on the work and progress of the institutions during the year for which the grants are made.

17. Recognition may be withdrawn for that year by the

Municipal Corporation of Delhi from any association or institution, if the association or institution violates or ceases to fulfil any of the conditions of recognition.

18. The recognition of an association or institution shall lapse if :

(a) a recognised institution or association ceases to exist, or an association or institution is transferred to a building or locality not already approved by the Municipal Corporation of Delhi;

(b) the association or institution is transferred to a different managing body not already approved by the Corporation.

The above rules and procedures for release of funds indicate how easy it is for organisations to get grants renewed by the Corporation. A certificate from the Councillor or private auditor is enough. A certificate from a private auditor is not difficult to obtain. Normally the accounts to be audited are so meagre and fee charged is so small that it makes easier for the organisation to get the funds audited. We also found that some of the voluntary organisations were not even registered under the Societies Registration Act 1868. Consequently, it came to our notice that some of the institutions did not have clearly defined objectives and activities.

Here are some examples of deviations from the laid down procedures. The Sant Parmanand Blind Relief Mission gets a recurring grant of Rs. 45,000 even though its management has been under attack and the grants are not used as an aid to improve the management. The Tirath Ram Shah Charitable Trust and Nursing Home were receiving Rs. 20,000 as grant annually while the records show that their beneficiaries belong to upper income group. The accounts department raised serious objections against giving grant to Dr. Shroff's Eye Hospital (grant of Rs. 80,000) and Sir Ganga Ram Hospital (grant of Rs. 80,000) on the ground that their financial position was quite sound. The Corporation Audit Report 1968-69 pointed to all these cases. But all the objections mentioned above had been overruled by the Standing Committee. Some of the institutions continue to receive grant irrespective of their eligibility for the same. On the other hand, the grants to the Lajpat Nagar Eye Hospital and St. Stephen's Hospital were withdrawn without assigning any reason.

There is a general feeling among the staff of the Health Department that association with social welfare organisations is one of the ways of climbing the "political ladder". Therefore, political leaders get themselves associated with these institutions and manage to secure grant for them from the Corporation. This in turn enhances their political status and support base.

Thus the existing procedure of budget formulation and grants-in aid indicates that the allocation of grant is "opportunity-based" rather than "need-based". Moreover, the Corporation is unable to provide regular support to the institutions. This affects the work of the institutions and the services they render to the community.

In order, therefore, to provide continuity of service and strengthen the foundations of the institutions, the Corporation would do well to set up a committee to select the voluntary organisations which deserve assistance.

Some of the members of the managing committees of the voluntary organisations, on the other hand, pointed out their difficulties in receiving the grant in time. The sanctioned amount was generally released at the end of the financial year. This delay in the release of grant and untimely disbursal of the grant created hardship to the grantee institution. This, however, is not peculiar to the health department of the Corporation alone. Therefore, it is very essential to improve on this old-fashioned procedure of releasing the sanctioned grant to the voluntary bodies. The Corporation would do well if it gave regular financial assistance to deserving welfare institutions and also extended its support for the new activities undertaken by them.

Medical Stores and Equipments

The procurement, development, maintenance and distribution of equipments and medicines constitute an important aspect of the financial management. Sometimes, the equipments are received from outside agencies. In this case the departmental authority is accountable for the specific items of equipment purchased from the funds, for the disposal of the equipment and the amount credited to the institution.

Table VIII.8 illustrates the magnitude of the activity involved in purchase of stores in respect of different hospitals. The figures also indicate rise in expenditure on equipment in Hindu Rao, Silver Jubilee and Victoria Zanana Hospital in 1969-70, whereas the amount spent on medicine remains constant.

Accounting and expenditure control, as well as the question of supplies are involved in the operation of these institutions. Health Department usually follows the traditional pattern of purchase through tenders and to distribute contracts widely as far as possible throughout the various business concerns in the metropolis. But the present trend is towards development of a central purchasing agency. The department is also following this approach of developing a central purchasing agency. This is further given an impetus by allowing the purchasing agency to inspect all goods delivered, to test all samples submitted, to transfer and dispose of any materials, equipment from operating agencies and to maintain a central warehouse.

Weighed against its advantages the disadvantages of the central purchasing agency are delay and red-tapism. The Deputy Health Officer (Medical) dealing with medicine and equipment worth Rs. 25,80,500 with the assistance of a single accountant is far from a satisfactory state of affairs.

Consequently, the time-barred medicines were found in Lajpat Nagar Hospital causing death of a boy from rabies. About two and a half lakh rupees remained unspent on drugs in the dispensaries of the South Delhi Zone. A large number of dispensaries complained of poor quality of medicines supplied to them. Except ordinary medicines no sulpha drugs were available in most of the dispensaries visited by the author. One man observed, "Public scold us for not giving them the proper drugs. But we know that we have no suitable drugs for influenza and cold in this winter season."

One of the solutions suggested to improve the purchase and distribution system is to appoint a Medical Officer to assist the Deputy Health Officer (Medical). The Department can

TABLE VIII.8

Provision for medicines/instruments and equipment/apparatus in hospitals and dispensaries during the years 1968-69 and 1969-70

(Rupees in lakhs)

Institutions	Medicines & Instruments				Equipment & Apparatus			
	1968-69		1969-70		1968-69		1969-70	
	actuals	%	actuals	%	actuals	%	actuals	%
Hindu Rao Hospital	5.50	28.7	6.50	28.9	3.00	58.7	2.00	37.6
S.J.T.B. Hospital	4.00	17.7	4.00	17.8	0.60	11.7	1.60	30.1
I.D. Hospital	0.90	4.0	1.00	4.4	0.05	1.0	0.10	1.9
General Hospital Shahdara	2.00	8.8	2.00	8.9	0.25	4.9	0.25	4.7
Victoria Zanana Hospital	1.75	7.7	1.75	7.8	0.90	17.6	1.00	18.8
G.L. Maternity Hospital	0.50	2.2	0.50	2.2	0.20	3.9	0.25	4.7
Balak Ram Hospital	0.35	1.5	0.35	1.5	0.05	0.1	0.005	0.1
Civil Hospital Shahdara	0.40	1.8	0.40	1.8	0.01	0.2	0.01	0.2
Colony Hospital (7)	2.25	9.9	2.00	8.9	0.01	1.9	0.10	1.9
Dispensaries (50)	4.00	17.7	4.00	17.8	—		—	
Total	21.65		22.50		5.07		5.315	

request the institutions that (i) they will maintain duplicate invoice of purchases made from the funds received from the central government, (ii) assume responsibility for any equipment purchased from these funds, (iii) indemnify the health department against any payment which the department might be required to make to the central government as a result of audit objections, concerning the use/disposition of inventories/equipment.

The central purchasing agency should also remember that the existence of the same is justified in terms of rendering service to a functional agency. Functional agency should take pains to clarify their need to the purchasing agency. A proper assessment of the requirement of medicines in the dispensaries should be made through an appropriate agency, e.g., the research wing of the department.

Economy

In view of the cuts in the budget, there are always some discussions and suggestions to economise. Any measure of economy in the health department relates to practices directly involving the agency's personnel. The Standing Committee in its proceedings on 3rd July, 1967, indicated various suggestions to reorganise various wings to economise departmental expenditure. It suggested reduction of all ad-hoc posts. Instead of having three D.H.Os. for malaria and smallpox eradication scheme, it suggested upgrading the present T.B. Control Officer to the post of Director of Communicable Diseases. It further suggested abolition of few posts of assistant surgeon grade-I doctors for T.B. Control Programme and T.B. Health Visitor in Shahdara thereby economising Rs. 8.20 lakhs. It also suggested economy of Rs. 2.50 lakhs by reducing 50 posts of sanitary inspectors. It also proposed a saving to the tune of Rs. 6 lakhs out of ad-hoc provisions for hospital service and dispensaries. Rupees six lakhs were proposed to be saved out of Rs. 50 lakhs on disposal operations, suggested by O&M Division. The personnel recruitment is a major problem in public health services. Any further economy might affect the efficiency of the department. It is worthwhile to carefully scrutinise the measures of economy before they are initiated, for the same may not affect the efficiency of the system.

Full Utilisation of Allocations

The usual common practice in any conventional administrative system is that an appropriation must be completely spent in order to demonstrate the administrative ability. But it does not appear to be the case with the health department. At times, the sanctioned amount is released only in March, which adversely affects the implementation of the programmes. In case of health services, where it is very difficult to predict the nature of emergency, it might not be possible to spend the sanctioned amount within a short stipulated period. At the same time, funds may not be available when they are needed. It is, therefore, important that the conventional procedure of sanctions and allocation of funds should give way to a more rational and systematic one.

Attitude to Government Responsibility

Closely related to the allocations and pattern of expenditure are some of the important questions such as : (a) What is actually needed? (b) The limits within which most people accept a policy? (c) What can be done from a financial and practical point of view? (d) What action should be taken and when? The views of the officials on some of the above mentioned questions were gathered during the interview.

Charging for Health Services

It is rather a controversial issue whether the services should be rendered free to all those who can pay and the people who are below a marginal line or they should be charged. Currently there are two formulas for charging the fees from the public : (a) flat rat and (b) in accordance with income. There are advantages and disadvantages of either of the formulas. But at the same time it appears an illogical and unsound proposition to give free medicines to the people. It may be noted here that every one felt that free distribution of medi-

Trend Of Expenditure Of Health Department In Relation To The Rise In Population In Delhi Municipal Corporation

Fig. VIII.3

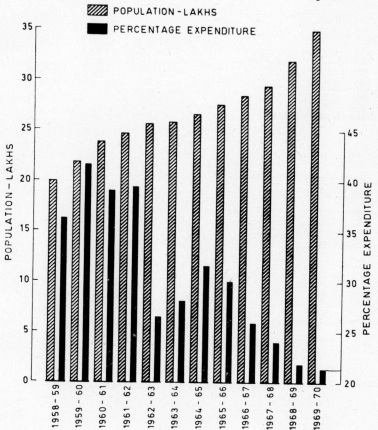

cines should be stopped. People should learn to pay for the services they need.

The views of the officials were divided on this issue. The executives felt that public should be charged at least ten to fifteen paise for each prescription card. They advocated this nominal charge for two reasons. Firstly it will reduce the undue crowd in the dispensaries for even the nominal charge will deter people from going to the dispensaries when they are not needed. Secondly, official prescription card once issued to the patient will be retained by the beneficiary, thus minimising the workload of the clerks.

The Health Officer, on the other hand, felt that the process of collection of revenue was cumbersome. He was, therefore, of the view that it should be left to the patients and not made compulsory. In deserving cases, it should be up to the Health Officer to offer free services. The whole concept of charity should give way to the concept of 'assistance' to the needy.

Revenue Collection

The health department is a welfare 'non-profit' department. It collects revenue in various ways to meet part of its expenses. Different services for which fees are charged are issuance of birth certificate, x-ray plate for anti-rabies treatment, from people drawing a monthly salary of Rs. 400/-. It was, however, observed that most people declared their income below Rs. 400/- with a view to evading payment.

Discussion

The effective use of the budget allocation can be meaningfully studied in relation to the services rendered to the people. It is difficult to quantify the performance of a medical care, for the satisfaction of the patients cannot be easily measured. However, it can be assessed in terms of the number of patients treated.

The general trend of increase in expenditure with the expansion of services is impressive, but it must be realised that this increase is in the face of rising costs and growing population. When seen in the light of the above factors, one can infer that there has been practically no net increase in investment since 1958-59. Taking the rise in population into consideration, there has been a slight decline in the per capita expenditure of the department.

A calculation based on the figures provided by 1961 Census and the Statistical Unit of the Corporation on the A.P. (Actual Population) Method indicates that per capita expenditure on health leaped from Rs. 11.18 in 1958-59 to Rs. 16.20 in 1968-69, while it was Rs. 13.20 in 1964-65. In the absence of any other reliable figure on present population in Delhi, it would be concluded that there has been no real rise in per capita expenditure on health services provided by the Corporation on account of the inflationary trends, the rise in the costs of goods and services. Besides, this precentage also includes expenditure on Family Planning, which received a boost in this period. It is, however, interesting to note that about 85 per cent of the total sums is spent on establishment, leaving only 15 per cent of the total revenue for services. It is also significant to note that while annual budget of one central government-run hospital in Delhi is Rs. 1.75 crores, the budget of the hospitals, clinics, dispensaries and family planning clinics run by the Corporation adds up to Rs. 2 crores. This points to the meagre resources provided to local health department for medical care programme.

A look at zonal distribution of funds reveals that allocation of budget for Shahdara Hospital was the lowest, whereas the need of that area was far greater. The zonal allocation of budget for Maternity and Child Welfare Centres indicates higher allocation in Civil Lines, City and South Delhi Zone, whereas it was meagre for Shahdara, West or Sadar Paharganj which were densely populated areas. Thus, the budget allocation in case of the respective areas indicated that the budget was neither based on the size of the population nor on the needs of the area and the people.

It is evident that budgeting is based mostly on the grants received from the Centre or other international body for a particular programme, rather than 'on need' pointed out by the zonal Councillors. The expenditure is "opportunity based" rather than "need based".

Comprehensive Financing of Health Services

Of all the problems involved in fiscal management of health, as reported by the officials and observed by the author, fragmentation is the most significant. The health services, as it appears, have been developed on a piecemeal basis by the authorities to meet any specific crisis on matter of intense public concern from time to time. Usually a specific financial arrangement is made for the case, without relating it to public services, which affects the total health of the people. Nor do we find any information to suggest that the financial arrangement has taken into account the patient and his family as a socio-economic unit. For example, family planning is given top priority in our national programme. It is yet to devise multi-dimensional approach to deal with socio-economic problem of the family. It is reported that malaria control and eradication of smallpox have been squeezed to make room for expenditure on family planning.

In Delhi, we hardly find any coordination between the child welfare services, welfare programmes, outpatient dispensaries, hospital for chronically sick patients, tuberculosis patients, society for physically handicapped, blind relief, school health programme and old-age services. Lack of coordination and integration among these services, with scarce financial resources at the disposal of the Corporation, results in failure to render maximum service to the people. Even at the Corporation level, different units are responsible for different but closely related subjects. Thus, lack of comprehensive budgeting leads to wastage of scarce funds at our disposal. For example, lack of auxiliary welfare services has resulted in increase in expenditure of hospitals. In Hindu Rao or Silver Jubilee T.B. Hospital, many patients stay beyond the period of actual medical care for they have no other place to go as there is no provision for the rehabilitation of the patients. There is no other welfare service agency to take care of them. The social service agencies like old people's homes or chronic sick convalescent homes could have very well taken up appropriate cases, relieving the burden on big hospitals. The school health programme without any agency to see whether prescription recommended for has been followed or not, is rendered incomplete and superficial.

Unless a comprehensive planning of welfare and health services is made at central, state and local levels, with focus on patients' total needs, it would be impossible to derive maximum return from the expenditure incurred on the services. Therefore, the financial management, directed towards the fulfilment of total objective, warrants reorganisation of the administrative system of the department with greater focus on preventive and after-care services.

CHAPTER IX

Public Relations

Public relations is deliberate, planned and sustained effort to establish, develop and maintain mutual relationships between role incumbents at various levels in an organisation, with a view to promoting harmony by dealing with individual and interpersonnel relational problems in an effective manner. Such relationships are vital not merely for individual performance but for organisational efficiency particularly when its goal is to render public service. Thus, in this framework we attempt to examine public relations problems of the health department.

The health department being a tax-supported agency, its existence depends on the desire of the community to maintain it. Moreover, in view of the modern concept of social service administration, the health department, at the local level, works "with the people" and not for them. Such interaction stimulates public cooperation which is an essential prerequisite for the implementation of any programme dealing with the people.

The need of public cooperation in health care is also an internationally recognised phenomenon. Current reports (Borsky and Sagen 1959) on America suggest that with increased interest in patient care in hospitals and chronically ill patients, the need for health education for outpatients

175

is also on the increase. At present, it is being increasingly realised that without the cooperation, interest and support of the patient little or nothing can be done to forestall disability or to restore, rehabilitate and prolong his functional and economic independence. There is thus a growing demand by hospitals and community administrators for health educators, adult education specialists, anthropologists to aid them in the task of actively involving the patients in their treatment and medical care.

Current Practices of Public Relations

With the setting up of the Corporation it was realised that the problems of urban development cannot be dealt with effectively without the active support of the people. Drawing from the experiences of the Rural Community Development Programmes, the Corporation ventured to take up Urban Community Development Programmes with a view to soliciting the support and cooperation of the people in implementing the programmes of development and welfare. This approach provided a new orientation to the programmes of the Corporation. For carrying out the task effectively the Corporation had set up departments of Social Education and Urban Community Development. These departments carried out the task until December 1966 when a Department of Community Services was set up combining various functions.

The Social Education Centres numbering 37 in different parts of the city and the Vikas Mandals (Citizens Development Councils) and Vikas Parishads (Neighbourhood Councils) numbering 62 are the forums to offer opportunity to the public to initiate and participate in programmes relating to the broad fields like health, sanitation, physical improvement and cultural programme. They also have Tele-clubs and other associations of different groups like Volunteer Corps, Bal Clubs, Mahila Mandals, etc., to carry on activities in their own field. Eventually in course of time, the Physical Education Section was separated from this department. By an office order no. 44/CES dated May 24, 1967 it was decided to adjust the placements of the personnel working in different sections of the Community Services.

The activities at present are spread out in different parts of the metropolis without any attachment to the zonal offices. With regard to public grievances, this department provides complaint cells in four zones, i.e., Town Hall, Karol Bagh, New Delhi South and Civil Lines Zone in addition to the head office. These cells are converted into control rooms during emergencies like flood, fire, heavy rain or epidemic. They operate round the clock during the emergency period.

Another department, which deals with public welfare, is the Slum Improvement Scheme of the Union Territory of Delhi with the enactment of the Slum Areas (Improvement and Clearance) Act 1956. The Slum Improvement Scheme provides for improvement of environmental conditions such as laying water-mains, sewers, provision of community latrines, baths, water taps, widening and paving of existing roads and lanes, providing street lighting, smokeless chullah and electrification. In the course of implementation the scheme was tranferred to D.D.A, on 22nd January, 1968. This section also has a great deal to do by way of improving their knowledge, outlook and habits in public health field.

A study of the working of the Public Relations Section of the Corporation reveals that the complaints are usually received by the Assistant Public Relations Officer, who maintains a liaison between the local press, public and the Corporation. He informs the tax-payers on the various new ventures of the Corporation. He also keeps the deliberative and executive wings of the Corporation informed about the news and views appearing in the press. He has to forward press clippings relating to difficulties of the people to the departmental heads concerned, for necessary action and report. He is ultimately responsible for the public relations programme of the Corporation.

At the zonal level, the complaints clerk combines the functions of the receptionist and the public relations man. The cyclostyled proformas for the complaints are maintained at the counter, wherein the public can register their grievances. These forms are later on sent to the respective officers, dealing with the case. A complaint can also be conveyed through telephone. But the usual experience was that the telephone line remained busy almost throughout the office hours. However, these reception counters act as clearing house for public grievances.

Besides this basic complaints section of the Corporation and community services section, each department, specially health, education and other social service sections practise public relations as a tool for management of their services. Before going into details of the Public Relations Programme it is necessary to identify some basic considerations for the implementation of the health programme.

Some Considerations in Health Programme

The success of the officials lies in setting a programme to the people and getting their acceptance for the same. For this, they need to contact prominent citizens, other officials and various key people in explaining the need of the programme for their acceptance. The planning for Public Relations requires a statement of the overall policy aims, objectives and programmes spelled out in a pamphlet, with a view to educating the people about the same. It also necessitates training in Public Relations, followed by evaluation of the programme.

While defining the concept 'public', we need to categorise it on the basis of religion, education, race and sex etc. Each programme also needs to be broken down into a smaller number of programmes to cover and cater to different sectors of the population.

It must be appreciated that Public Relations is a two-way process. It involves flow of information, reactions, understanding not only from agency to public but also in the reverse direction. The Health Department may have the appreciation from the press, business groups and professionals for its performance but that image may be tarnished if the people deprecate the programme.

It is also necessary to take note of certain impediments to public relations in Health Department. One must admit that people are rarely interested in "public health" and they are at best concerned with personal health and that of the members of their family. "It is in fact more than a little distressing to find that an appreciable percentage of the population is quite ignorant of the existence of the field." (Hanlon : 314) Even in highly developed countries like the U.K. and the U.S.A., studies reveal that public are indifferent and ignorant of existing health services.

Another obstacle accrues from the professional nature of the job. The personnel involved in health services usually get too much involved in the nature of the work done and ignore the human factors involved in it. This gives rise to human relations problems both with the organisation and between the staff and the public.

It should also be recognised that a great many contacts with health department are unwilling contacts, like taking injections, medicine, vaccination and other immunization measures or to obtain birth or death certificate etc. This makes it all the more necessary for the health department to establish more cordial relations with the people.

Methods of Good Public Relations

We may also indicate some accepted measures and methods of public relations in Health Department. The Health Department exists to serve the public, and hence there is direct interaction between the staff and the people. If a staff member fails to establish cordial relations with the citizen, it may result in poor image of the department and adversely affect the work of the department. At the same time if the employees are dissatisfied and have a negative attitude towards the department, it may be reflected in their disposition to their work and the citizens and again impair the image of the civic body in general and the department in particular. The success of the public relations programmes lies not only in fostering harmonious relations between the citizens and the officials but also among themselves. For relationship between the interacting parties, it is essential to have effective communications.

Every organisation, whatever its size may be, should therefore make provision for some information desk. The person in charge of the information desk should be knowledgeable and well trained in human relations. A common cause of ill-feeling towards the official is the manner in which visitors or clients are frequently shunted from one place to another. No one takes the trouble to ascertain what people exactly need. The person manning the Information Counter should also have the referral responsibility. Another way of improving public relations could be by coordinating certain services and activities and by decentralizing the location of places, where the people must come. What is needed most is the change in the attitude of the officials rather than merely structural changes.

Every public agency is bound to receive complaints and suggestions. It should be open and receptive to such criticism for it provides feedback for effecting the required changes and modifications in the programmes and policies and also inspire confidence among the citizens about the genuineness of the organisation. However, in order to create and sustain the confidence of the people, it is essential that the organisation should devise mechanisms to deal with such grievances and complaints.

Avenues of Publicity

It is essential to educate the public about the available services, for that is critical for sound public relations. Mass media like local press, radio and television are important channels and should be used for the purpose. Likewise, exhibits, film strips, street car and bus advertisement, comic books and paid advertisements are some other useful media for public education.

Annual audit reports are sometimes considered as methods of developing good public relations. Involving the community groups and voluntary associations are other important methods of gaining public support. In brief, the community workers have to closely interact with people in order to establish meaningful relations with them.

Evaluation of Practices Adopted

Against this background if we examine the present practices of handling grievances and complaints it was revealed that they are far from satisfactory. It was observed that the staff at the counter were indifferent to public enquiries and they usually took very long time to provide the needed information. For instance, such cases were found common wherein the public had to move from counter to counter to obtain routine information on birth certificate or polio and other vaccine. "Every one was up to passing on the baby" was the response of many respondents. Reception Counter is almost non-existent in the hospitals. During the field work many patients complained that queues were ignored by the staff to extend favours.

As regards Reception Centres, it was observed that they were housed in dilapidated buildings. In most cases, these were housed in residential localities without proper working atmosphere and sanitary facilities. The premises of the Zonal Office presented a poor look in this respect. For example, the main corridor of the Zonal Office had the stain of 'chewed pan spits'. No spittoons or other essentials were provided for and no posters were displayed.

Dealing with Public Complaints

On enquiring about the manner in which public complaints are dealt with in the department, the administrators pointed out that more than a thousand complaints were received in a month. Complaints were usually sent to the Health Officer. An analysis of the complaints revealed that 70 per cent of them related to drain blockage and irregular visit of the sweepers in their premises, whereas about 20 per cent related to neighbours' misdeeds, and the rest 10 per cent concerned the behaviour of the health officials, delay in receiving some certificate, dearth of particular medicine at times in certain dispensaries etc. It is, however, significant that most of these complaints were personal and did not pertain to community problems.

Ninety per cent of the staff reported that these complaints were usually referred to the higher authorities for necessary action. In case of local complaints by the Councillors, action was taken at an early opportunity. In regard to cases of general nature and meant for referral to higher authorities, one had to wait for months, even for a formal acknowledgement. Not only the public but the lower level staff was also dissatisfied about the delays. In case of the employees, it was pointed out that most of their requests for improving their working conditions were turned down by the higher officials. For example, during the study period, it was observed that the water pipe of a Health Centre was defective and remained unattended for three months in spite of several reminders by Health Officer.

It was generally felt that it was of no avail to call attention to the shortcomings of the department, as nobody took them seriously. This adversely affected public relations. One of the suggestions offered to improve the position was to open a complaint cell under a Senior Medical Officer, who would work as a coordinator for different wings of the department for follow up of public grievances in regard to medical care and environmental sanitation.

Field Contacts

In regard to field contacts, instances were reported where the citizens resented the multiplicity of calls by health visitor, malaria worker, vaccinator and family planning worker in the household. The public get vexed and say, "Don't you have any other work but to lecture us around." In the absence of any procedure to follow up a particular case on discharge from the hospital or maternity home, the call by different workers, erratically at various times of the year, tends to create dissatisfaction among the public. The department could do well to start correspondence with the public in order to establish contact with them rather than a casual visit once a while to mark their presence. Only intra-departmental co-ordination can bring solution to this problem, where one section would be informed about the programme of the other section and they would plan their visit accordingly.

It has been pointed out earlier that the Corporation has no systematic public relations nor planned employee training programme. Unless the employees are provided with opportunity for development and for better prospects, they would not be prompted to employ their abilities fully and do their best. It is, therefore, essential that the employees should be made to feel themselves a part of the organisation and also their future development and prospects should be assessed. He should be made to feel that he is working for something higher than mere earning his livelihood.

Health Education

The avenues of publicity used by the Corporation are far from adequate. Corporation health education programme is too fragmentary to make effective use of the radio, television and press. It is interesting to note that the Corporation has not published its annual reports since 1963. The Public Rela· tions Officer was under suspension and retired since 1969. It was observed that the Corporation did not have much publishing material about its health programmes. On Family Planning, it is rare to find posters on the health education aspect of it. All these facts go to suggest that the Health Department does not place any special emphasis on public relations, excepting what is being followed and practised by the general administration section of the Corporation. It was also revealed that no special attempt was being made by the Health Department to make the public aware of the services and programmes, so that they might benefit from them.

It was also observed that in the absence of any written policy on public relations, the Corporation staff used personal discretion to extend favour to the people. It was also seen that lack of public relations training, officiousness and rigidity resulted in harassment to the Public and proved detrimental to their programme performance. public cooperation and participation in the programme is most vital particularly when it is intended to cater to the needs of the people and it is to be executed in a democratic framework. The efficiency of the civic administration depends not only on the organisational structure, financial resources and personnel, but also on participation of the people whom it caters. But public cooperation will be forthcoming only when people are aware of the programme and are convinced of its usefulness. Thus, the perceptions and evaluations of the people about the programme in vogue become very important.

Beneficiaries' View towards Health Department

Originally it was decided to select a colony hospital in South Delhi Zone and (taking 1965 as the mean period of last ten years of its functioning) to interview every twentyfifth patient admitted in the year (as appeared in the hospital register). On interviewing, it was found that a large number of them had shifted from the said area. It was also decided to select fifty patients on the basis of random sample. But even that did not work, since the patients were drawn from poorer sections of the community and both husband and wife were employed and did not have time to spare for the interview.

The author, therefore, relied on the studies of the Indian Institute of Public Administration (on citizen and administration). In an attempt to test the validity of some of their findings the author interviewed about twenty patients in the outdoor department of the urban health centre and the prominent citizens. No tall claims are made on the basis of survey. However, it does point to the perceptions and evaluations of the people about the health services, which is surely useful to plan and organise the programmes. It is interesting to note that majority of the beneficiaries in the outdoor clinics were not actually aware of the services rendered by the Corporation. They were also faced with difficulties in getting the services of the Health Department.

Similarly the I.I.P.A. study (Barnabas 1965 : 27-28) reports the deliberate delay, harassment and discourtesy in many departments of the Corporation and ends up with a suggestion to develop better communication between public and officials on administrative procedure.

Another study on "Citizens' Grievances in Development Administration" (Barnabas 1966 : 48) points to the poor public image of the Family Planning and Maternity and Child Welfare Centres in Delhi. In a study on "Existing Machinery and Procedure for Redress of Citizens' Grievances", Jagannadham (1967) reports, "It is not merely the complexity of rules and procedures that lead to delay, but laxity of administration and supervision, lack of interest and of spirit of responsibility towards public interest may be some of the other contributory factors." Also a study on "Citizen and Municipal Bureaucracy" (Jagannadham 1971) revealed that delay, corruption, rudeness and discourtesy contribute a great deal towards the formation of an unfavourable image of local self government institutions in the metropolis.

The I.I.P.A. study on the "Public Image of Hospital

Administration", though limited in scope, attempts to provide people's image of medical care in Delhi. The field of study was Lady Hardinge Hospital and Irwin Hospital covering population of the Corporation area. Its findings are particularly relevant to this study and a few of these are reported below :

(i) Dissatisfaction was expressed about the poor quality of food, lack of care and doctors' preoccupation with so many other cases. Most of the beneficiaries preferred private practitioner or maternity and child health centre to the hospital.

(ii) A good percentage of people worry about lack of medical care in the hospital. The patients feel that the doctors have no time, and on occasions even avoid meeting patients. About 52 per cent of old cases narrated that they were afraid of doctors as they had very little time to devote for the patients; 48 per cent of the respondents felt that they were satisfied with the doctors' attention to their ailment.

(iii) Another major cause of the dissatisfaction and grievance among public against medical care is the hazard of standing in queue in outdoor department. About 88 per cent of the respondents confirmed this complaint.

It is interesting to find that no one complained of lack of drugs or poor doctor-patient ratio or nurse-patient ratio and other administrative problems but of their personal discomfort and worry. Commenting on the behaviour of officials, a local newspaper remarked, "Inordinate delay, indifference, complete apathy and often rudeness—these are what the ordinary man has to put up with at most of the hospitals. If the patient is unsophisticated, his travails are greater. Nobody is even prepared to show him the way to the right department." This was said to be true for both Corporation and Central or State managed hospitals.

The Hospital Review Committee (1968) observed about the Corporation hospitals, "Scant regard for sanitation (for instance, dead tissues, soiled dressings, etc., are thrown on open garbage dumps), inadequate sterilization facilities, like putting soiled bandages in the sun for sterilization, deplorable ambulance services—with all vehicles out of order on most days."

Another local newspaper (*Statesman* of 18-2-1968) observed, "The problem of too few doctors trying to cope with too many patients is not unique in Delhi and cannot be cited as an excuse for the heart-breaking inefficiency, apathy, rudeness and callousness encountered by countless patients who need sympathy and gentle handling as much as they do medical relief. Nor is the appalling condition of ambulances attributable to too much demand; one hospital has had the dubious distinction of reporting that all the ambulance vehicles were out of order on most days in 1968. Perhaps, the most telling comment on capital's medical aid was the case of the municipal councillor, who, on taking his ailing mother to Irwin Hospital, received the gratuitous advice to take the old lady away from this 'butchery' to a private clinic."

Public Image of Conservancy Work

A study (S.B. Singh 1967) of certain areas like Madangir Khadar, Srinivaspuri, etc., reveals, "No arrangement has been made for underground sewage. Surface drains get clogged creating breeding place for mosquitoes and flies. The condition of latrines is the worst imaginable. The arrangement for clearance of filth and garbage is very inadequate. Under these conditions, it is impossible for people to lead a normal healthy life."

Officials' Opinion

The officials belonging to different cadres reported lack of public cooperation as one of their major difficulties. Analysis of their replies indicated that public attitude towards health services was of two kinds, viz., (i) positive, and (ii) negative.

In view of free medical care, the public tend to demand institutional service irrespective of the seriousness of their ailment. For example, even for ordinary cough or stomach trouble they would rush to the dispensary, creating difficulty for more seriously sick patients. Sometimes they want to get things done expeditiously without going through the required formalities. This is more so in case of the sophisticated patients. Sometimes, they try to bribe the chowkidar and get into the first row of the queue. They do not like to observe rules and wish to have preferential treatment for their individual case.

Commenting on this aspect a newspaper reported the grossly disproportionate attention claimed and commandeered by the vast army of VIPs. "The best medical brains often hang around hypochondriac Ministers, not always involuntarily, while their normal work suffers, as do ordinary patients. In the last session of Parliament, the Union Health Minister assured angry MPs that in the State-run hospitals and nursing homes, they will have preference irrespective of the seriousness of their ailments over the people they are supposed to represent and serve. Some years ago, a patient nearly died because the life-saving machine, urgently needed, had to be fetched from a ministerial home where it was being kept just in case." These all illustrate people's attitude towards personal health care services.

Negative Attitude

The people also have negative attitude to public health programmes. The staff of health clinics reported about public apathy particularly towards immunization and vaccination programme. This is more in the areas inhabited by the lower income groups and slum dwellers. For example, in Kotla Mubarakpur a vaccinator found himself baffled with young children and mothers who were hiding themselves behind the curtain or door when he visited them. The author also observed mothers running away with children in arms on an inoculation drive day. It was pointed out that there were quite a significant number of children without primary vaccination. On the contrary, the citizens in Defence Colony or South Extension themselves ring up the Zonal Officer and request him for vaccination. But those who need immunization service most show a constant resistance to all these programmes.

Another area of negative public cooperation, as observed by the officials, was in food hygiene operations. The Public Health authority at the zonal level found it very difficult to deal with bye-laws regarding licensing of shops and food stalls because of lack of public cooperation. The food squad consisting of only 10 people could demolish a stall. But it could not follow it up unless the local people cooperated with them. It was commonly observed that foodstuffs were sold in unhygienic conditions near primary and secondary schools. The school teachers did not dissuade children from buying those exposed foodstuffs. One Zonal Health Officer pointed out that in the absence of any public witness against the shopkeeper with adulterated food, all the efforts of the health staff to detect food adulteration failed to yield the required results. The people are usually indifferent and do not assume their responsibility. Pointing to this a Zonal Health Officer in charge of Public Health observed, "Public actually do not attach any importance to us. We are considered as the doctors of the flies and the mosquitoes." These comments indicate that Zonal Health Officers have a low status which impedes them in their role performance.

Health education programme also received a setback owing to lack of cooperation from the teachers and other school staff. It was pointed out that most of the suggestions made by the Health Officer were not followed at all.

Field workers also had similar experiences. They found public indifference to the community health and sanitation programme. This was more true of the labour colonies. The work force in Delhi is largely drawn from the countryside of the neighbouring States of Uttar Pradesh, Rajasthan and Punjab. They bring along with them rural habits and take time to learn new ways. For example, the migrants, who had not been assimilated with the city culture, did not find it convenient to use public latrine and contributed to the insanitary conditions in the city. This was observed in areas of Ashram, Kotla and Nanakpura, where public come to relieve themselves on both sides of Ring Road, the main road of the metropolis.

All these things indicate a gap between the public health programmes on the one hand and the needs of the citizens on the other. It is evident that much of the problem of sanitation in the city could be attributed to lack of civic consciousness and apathy of the people. Moreover, there is a general helplessness and indifference towards the shortcomings of municipal government and hence even enlightened and active citizens do not assume any responsibility and venture to rectify the situation or mobilize efforts to deal with it. All this leads to ineffective service implementation.

Health Department and Voluntary Organisations

That the voluntary organisations did not extend cooperation to the Corporation was also evident from a visit to the squatters colonies in Janakpura and Seemapuri. No Government or voluntary organisation has yet come forward to help the residents with any welfare programme. The children in these colonies live in most uncongenial conditions, unsuitable for their proper growth. Police have opened a juvenile aid bureau in Seemapuri but there is no plan to run it in a successful manner, either by the Indian Council of Child Welfare or the State Welfare Department. The voluntary agencies could have performed a positive role by taking up preventive as well as ameliorative roles which have not been taken up by the Corporation. In Nangloi, a foreign mission has started a dispensary and a balwadi, whereas no voluntary body had till then come forward to assist them. Nor the Corporation has any social service agency to serve in the area. The State Social Welfare Board has also failed to make any headway in bringing the welfare agencies to the uncovered areas.

Pointing to the role of the voluntary organisations, some of the top executives felt that they did not perform a positive role as expected of them. They could have made their contribution by supplementing the efforts of the Corporation by educating the people about various programmes and also by mobilizing their support for their implementation. The Corporation also do not encourage other bodies to come up to help them in their efforts.

In view of the various problems concerning public relations, there is an urgent need to have a well defined policy. Furthermore, there is need to have provision for training and

staff development. The doctors and paramedical staff should
be trained in human relationship. This should be supplemen-
ted by employing social care workers for different medical
institutions. Here we quote from Seabom Committee Report
(1968) regarding the usefulness of employing social workers in
health field:

"It is a paradox that cooperation between workers in the
medicine and other social services could often be poor when
both are so dependent on communication and they are so
involved in common concerns. Medicine and social work
share responsibilities in the field of disturbed personal relationships and social maladjustment. They are both much
involved in helping with the consequences of poverty and
deprivation. The problems of living with chronic diseases
(which dominates the practice of medicine today) often
are medical-social... But doctors have been slow in coming
to terms with the new concept 'social work helping profession' that is growing so rapidly alongside them. Together,
they might be more effective in diagnosis as well as providing support and care for many serious social and emotional
difficulties which cannot at present be offered at."

Response to Public Suggestions

However good public relations with personnel development
programme be, it cannot replace the need to make local bodies
a strong and efficient instrument for serving the people and
meeting their requirements.

The Maude Committee on Management of Local Government (1967) opined, "The real strength of local authority is
the local public and this means a personal relationship, a state
of affairs in which the public feel that the local authority and
local public service belong to them."

The element of universalism of social administration is observed in Maude Committee's suggestion that the organisation
must be sensitive to the needs of the citizens and there should
be clear facilities for grievances to be heard. The members of
the public should feel that they have avenues of appeal and
clearly defined sources of information. The private individual

should not feel that his only contact with local authority is at election time, when the councillors approach them for votes. For this reason, it is suggested by the Municipal authorities that the complaint sections of the Zonal Offices of the Corporation as well as the Public Relations Department of the Corporation should be given better status and put in charge of responsible staff, who can really inform the public of various procedures and send the complaints in proper time. It was felt that one complaint cell should be attached to the Town Hall with a senior officer in charge as coordinator of services. Similarly, the Zonal Office should have one Complaint Officer and assistant for follow up.

Lastly, we come to the problem of educating the public which is vital for the success of any public programme. Citizens must be educated about health bye-laws and their adherence to them should be ensured. Cooperation with the voluntary organisations, central health education bureau, medical colleges and teachers' training institutes would go a long way in realising the goals. However, there is need to revitalise the health education section of the Corporation as a unified section. The Corporation Health Officer should make effective use of the mass media through close cooperation with the publicity department of the Corporation and Delhi Administration.

The need for public cooperation in successful implementation of any welfare programme can hardly be emphasized. This can be achieved by educating the people and mobilizing their support. Again, this calls for systematic assessment of the needs of the people and evolving the programmes in tune with them. Thus, public relations have a vital role to play in realising these objects.

CHAPTER X

Overview and Suggestions

Our analysis in the foregoing chapters clearly suggests that the civic body is faced with a variety of problems, in coping with the growing health needs of the city. In the wake of growing industrial and commercial activities the population of the city is increasing at a rapid pace and at the same time the health problems are becoming complex in character, calling for a new approach. But the politico-administrative structure is not remodelled to suit the new needs nor are the resources being mobilized to combat the complex problems.

The problems of health services do not merely relate to expansion of the existing services and creation of new services, but also relate to proper allocation and distribution, keeping in view the diverse needs of the population. At the same time, the civic body has to deal with problems of environmental sanitation, air pollution, adulteration of food articles and medicines. But perhaps, the most vital of all these problems is imparting health education to the citizenry, so that they are able to utilize the available services and also to play their role in creating and maintaining proper physical conditions required for a city.

In order to realise these goals of providing better environmental sanitation and cleanliness and health services to the people, the civic body has to reorient its policies and programmes, mobilize resources, reallocate the existing amenities and services, coordinate its activities, create new machinery or to activise the existing one to enforce the policies and programmes to yield desired results and above all to evolve an effective programme of health education. Before we enumerate various measures that the civic government has to take in order to provide better health services in the city of Delhi, it would be appropriate to briefly recapitulate some of the main problems in this area. Briefly stated, these are as follows :

1. The city has witnessed a very rapid growth of population, particularly after the partition of India in 1947. This led to a mass exodus of people to the city. The population has continued to increase since then. The census of 1971 has also shown an increase during the decade (1961-71). It is estimated that by the next census the population of the city would out-strip the figure anticipated in the Master Plan of the city. This unanticipated growth of population has severely affected the health services as all other amenities.

It must also be noted that about half of the population of the city is below the age of 19 years and as such needs more medical care.

2. Closely related to the growth of population is its distribution. The density of population has serious implications for the organisation of health services. It has been indicated that the population is unevenly distributed in the city. Some of the areas are more thickly populated compared to others. For instance, the areas of City Sadar and Paharganj are more thickly populated compared to other areas of the walled city and New Delhi. The areas which are more thickly populated also show high incidence of disease and at the same time they are lacking in medical facilities. Thus, the areas of the city which need relatively more facilities have lesser of them. Not only that the facilities are wanting in certain areas of the city, but the resources and space impose serious constraints on creating more facilities. For instance, it is not possible to provide more garbage places in some of the areas or set up dispensaries for want of space.

It is also brought out that the deployment of sanitary staff like the sweepers is also not related to the needs of different areas. The medical facilities are unevenly distributed and have no relation with the real needs of various parts of the city.

3. Unplanned growth of population has given rise to unplanned habitation in the form of jhuggies and unauthorised colonies. These areas are generally inhabited by poor people, living in rather unhygienic conditions and do not have access to medical facilities. There are over 200 such colonies which do not have medical facilities nor does the civic body take responsibility of their cleanliness. Such localities not only pose problems of health and sanitation to the people living there but to the neighbouring areas and the city as a whole.

4. It has also been pointed out that about 1.50 lakh people migrate to the city from rural areas of the neighbouring states. These people add to the population of the city and thereby cause strain on the existing civic amenities. Apart from that these people also bring rural habits with them which are quite opposed to the values of urban life. They are, therefore, not able to make use of the existing amenities. On the contrary, they adopt a way of life which proves dysfunctional to the development of the city. Jhuggies in and around some of the residential areas and also small dairies therein are good examples of that.

5. Apart from the growth and complexity of population in the metropolis, which have implications for the organisation of the health services, the present administrative set up too is not very conducive for it either. The health services, as indicated earlier, are managed by several bodies like the Municipal Corporation, Delhi Administration, New Delhi Municipal Committee and the Central Government and other autonomous bodies like Delhi Development Authority and others, and as such it becomes difficult to coordinate the services provided by the various bodies. The available resources are not utilized to the best advantage of the people, for there is good deal of overlap and duplicity of services. Also certain sections of the population have an access to all types of medical facilities whereas others are completely deprived of the same.

Like the organisation and management of the health services, the duplicity of administrative structure also creates problems with regard to environmental sanitation. As pointed out earlier, there are several residential areas for the sanitation and cleanliness of which no authority assumes responsibility. It is revealed that in some of the newly developed colonies there is no arrangement for even sweeping on a regular basis. It has also been observed that industrial units have been set up in the residential areas which are hazardous for the health of the people. In the present set up, there is no appropriate administrative machinery to deal with this problem, which not only threatens the health of the people today but is likely to assume serious proportions in course of time.

6. Closely related to the administrative system is the political style of leadership which has a close bearing on the existing health services in the city. It has been observed that political rivalries and competition have not merely affected the health services but the entire amenity structure. The political leaders instead of formulating broad policies and programmes for the development of civic amenities for the city in general and health services in particular exert their influence in getting more services for their constituents. The influencial ones succeed in getting greater share allocated to their areas. This results in regional imbalances and also makes the deprived citizenry hostile to the civic administration. Furthermore, this narrow outlook of the leadership affects the entire policy-making and planning which apparently seems to be the case in Delhi.

7. It has been revealed that the local government has not been able to evolve policies and programmes for providing health services consistent with the needs of the city. This has been largely because of the lack of autonomy of the local government. Although, formally the local government may appear to be autonomous but in reality its autonomy is undermined by higher levels of government, which are held by a different political party. For instance, the Jan Sangh has been in power in the Municipal Corporation but the Metropolitan Council is held by the Congress Party. The political diversity at different levels of government creates a good deal of rivalry and competition which is detrimental for effective functioning of the local government.

8. Defused administrative structure and fragmented politics has severely affected the bureaucratic performance. The

bureaucrats instead of being committed to the institutional programmes have shifted their commitment and loyalties to the influential individuals and thereby undermined the goals of the system. This has eroded the faith of the people in the services provided by the local body. It is evident from the fact that the services rendered by the local body do not enjoy good reputation. It is our common experience that a citizen would not like to go to the municipal dispensary if he can afford to pay the fees to a private practitioner.

9. Apart from the politico-administrative set up, the efficiency of the technical staff is also affected by the service conditions. It has been pointed out that the medical service is many times constrained by the non-availability of adequate equipments, medicines and staff etc. Their performance is also restrained by long drawn procedures which they have to follow in the discharge of their duties. Considering the nature of the emergent situation in which they have to operate, these rigidly laid down procedures not only slow down their performance but render them ineffective.

It has also been revealed that the staff engaged in the organisation and management of the health services is not provided with amenities commensurate with the arduous work they have to put in. This particularly applies to the sanitary and medical staff. The employees in this category had expressed a good deal of dissatisfaction with their work.

10. It has been observed that the planning and organisation of health services not only show regional imbalance but they are not based on any rational considerations also. Partly they are governed by political pulls and pressures, as already indicated, but partly it is also due to the fact that no systematic information is available about health needs of various areas. Although habitation pattern in the city does indicate economic division of the population, yet no health statistics are available on that basis. It has been found that there are certain areas which show greater incidence of certain types of diseases, yet no systematic information on these lines has been collected by the local body. Thus, it is observed that plans and programmes for health services are not guided by any rational consideration.

The local government has not been in a position to maintain the public health services at the same level as in the past, leave alone their expansion. This is largely due to its tight financial position. But even the available resources have not been rationally allocated in relation to the needs of the various areas and the kind of services required.

An analysis of the expenditure on health services clearly brings out the fact that the expenditure on medical relief has remained more or less consistent since 1950-59. In view of the rising cost of medicine and equipment it is not possible to maintain the level of service in course of time. It has also come to notice that on certain items like public health and scavenging of drains the expenditure has been considerably curtailed which clearly suggests that these important aspects of health services have been ignored. Considering the changing composition of the population and public apathy, the public health and health education programmes should have been strengthened and more funds should have been allocated for these programmes. But strangely, the reverse has happened.

11. It is well known that no programme of social services can be effective without public support and cooperation. This is perhaps more true in case of health services, for the best medical and health services and also the sanitation and cleanliness programme may fail to yield desired results for want of public support and cooperation. And to ensure public support and cooperation, it is essential to have effective public health education programme and involve the voluntary organisations in carrying out various activities related to health and sanitation. It is brought out that voluntary organisations are not actively involved in the current health programmes in Delhi. The newly formed Federation of Hospital Welfare Associations in the Union Territory of Delhi is a bold and progressive step towards integrating all hospital welfare services in the capital.

In brief, it can be said that the organisation and management of health services in Delhi face a variety of problems which are social, demographic, administrative and financial in nature. Therefore, it is essential to think of an integrated approach, keeping in view various factors, if the medical and health services are to be made more meaningful. Some of the specific suggestions in this regard are as follows :

1. The growing population size is really posing a serious threat to the organisation and management of social services in general and health services, in particular. No city can plan and organise services effectively for an ever growing population. In view of this, the planners have to decide on an optimum population which the city can cater to in the light of its available service infrastructure and resources. Alongside restricting the population size, due consideration has also to be given to the needs of various sections of the population. It has been well brought out that different sections of the city population need different types of services to which they do not have access at present. And also certain areas which have not grown in a planned manner suffer for want of these services all the more. In order, therefore, to strike a proper balance, special services have to be initiated and organised for the deprived and rather underdeveloped pockets of the city.

2. It is difficult to think of coordination of the existing services and their effective utilization with the present administrative system which is highly fragmented and defused. The present administrative system is not merely responsible for its ineffectiveness but also accounts for under-utilization and waste of scarce resources. It is, therefore, essential to have a well-knit system of health administration with functional linkage within and between various sub-units responsible for providing medical and health services in the capital.

3. In a democratic polity, the administrative system can be effective only when the political leaders confine themselves to planning and policy-making and have closer touch with their constituents. The leadership seems to be failing in formulating realistic and meaningful programmes, for they do not have close touch with the people. It is also seen that instead of evaluating their plans and policies and gathering meaningful information for making them effective they take to personalised styles and cater to the needs of certain individuals or a section rather than the community as a whole. It is, therefore, essential that the political leaders establish close relations with their constituents and devote their ener-

gies and efforts and formulate plans and policies to cater to the needs of the total population and for the balanced growth of the city rather than work for a section of their supporters only. The political leaders have to win the confidence of the people and strengthen the system rather than wield and consolidate personal power if we really wish to make the administrative system more effective.

4. In order to develop effective programmes, we have to do a good deal of experimentation, for that alone can help us in developing realistic programmes. Considering the heterogeneity of the population and diversity of needs of the people, such experimentation becomes all the more essential. In view of the limitation of resources and rigidity of the system, it becomes difficult for any bureaucratic organisation to take up such a work. Apart from openness and flexibility in the system, the individuals handling these experimentations have to be committed and dynamic which a bureaucratic system may not offer. It is, therefore, felt that such a task may be assigned to the voluntary organisations. The voluntary organisations can play a very effective role in a democratic polity and recognising their role, the local government must actively involve them both in carrying out experimentation and informing policy making and planning. The social service programme, whether health or family planning or education, can be successful only with the involvement of the community through integrated community approach. The role of committed social workers along with the political leaders has to be recognised in building up a unified coordinated community approach in health administration.

Selected References

Acts and Codes

Cantonment Act, 1924.
Constitution (Seventh Amendment) Act, 1956.
Constitution (Fourteenth Amendment) Act, 1962.
Delhi Corporation Act, 1957.
Delhi Administration Act, 1966.
Delhi Corporation Amendment Act, 1959.
Delhi Administration (Business) Rules Act, 1966.
Delhi Development Act, 1965.
Government of India Act, 1919.
Government of India Act, 1935.
Government of Part C States Act, 1951.
Government of Union Territories Act, 1963.
Municipal Corporation of Delhi—Manual of Bye-laws (Third Edition), 1967.
Prevention of Food Adulteration Act, 1954.
Punjab Municipal Act, 1911.
Slum Areas Act, 1956.
Territorial Councils Act, 1956.
Union Territories (Laws) Act, 1950.

Books & Articles

Abel Smith Brian and Titmuss, *The Cost of National Health*

Services in England and Wales, Cambridge (Cambridge University Press, 1956).

Adie, David C., *"Responsibility of the State in the Supervision of Public Welfare Programme"* Social Science Review (December, 1939).

Adrian, Charles R., Governing Urban America, Structure, *Politics and Administration* (New York, McGraw Hill, 1955).

American Public Health Association, *What is the score of evaluation of local public health services* (New York, The Association, 1950).

Anderson, Ronald and Anderson, O.W., *"A Decade of Health Services"* (University of Chicago Press, Chicago, London, 1967).

Anderson, William and Weidnon, E.W., *American City Government,* revised edition (New York, Holt, 1950).

Aronson, Albert, *The Application of Business Techniques to the Administration of a Social Agency in Administration, Supervision and Consultation,* Papers from 1954 Social Welfare Forum, National Conference of Social Work (Family Service Publication, New York, 1955).

Baker, Benjamin, *Urban Government* (Von Nostrand, New York, 1965).

Bartlett, H.M., *Social Work Practice in the Health Field* (National Association of Social Workers, New York, 1961).

Bennis, G. Warren, Problem-orientated administration (*Hospital Administration,* Winter, 1960).

Bishop, J., *Hospital Central Service Department* (a guide to functions, organisations, service, 1963).

Bhattacharya, M., *Essays on Urban Government* (Metropolitan Book Depot, New Delhi, 1969).

Bopagamage, A., *Delhi, a study in Urban Sociology* (University of Bombay, Bombay, 1957).

Borkar, G., *Health in independent India* (Ministry of Health, Govt. of India, New Delhi, 1957).

Btish, S., *"Utilisation of health service for hospital"* Medical Care (Vol. III, No. 1, 1966).

Bulsara, Jal F., *Problems of rapid urbanization in India* (Popular Prakashan, Bombay, 1964).

Chandra, J.P., *Delhi—A Political Study* (Metropolitan Book Co., Delhi, 1969).

Cohen, Emeline W., *Autonomy and delegation on country government, a study of delegation in education and local health administration* (Institute of Public Administration, London, 1952).

Confrey, Eugene A., *Administration of Community Health Services* (International City Managers Association, Chicago, 1961).

Davies, J.O.F. et al., *Towards a measure of Medical Care, operational research in health services—a symposium* (Nuffield Provincial Hospital Trust, Oxford University Press, 1962).

Dimock, Marshall E., *Administrative vitality* (Harper and Brothers, New York, 1959).

Dalal, Dhandulal, *Municipal Finance*, Local Self Government Institute (Horiman Circle, Fort, Bombay, 1957).

Donnison, D.V. and Chapman, V., *Social policy and administration* (Allen and Unwin, London, 1965).

Duncan, O.D. et al., *Social Research on Health* (New York Social Science Research Council, New York, 1946).

Dutt, P.R., *Rural Health Services in India* (Ministry of Health, Govt. of India, New Delhi, 1962).

Eckstien, H., *English health service, its origin, structure and achievements* (Harvard University Press, Massachusetts, 1954).

Elderveld, S.J., Jagannadham, V. and Barnabas, A.P., *The Citizen and the Administration in a developing democracy* (I.I.P.A., New Delhi, 1968).

Evang, Karl, *Present day health services in their relation to medical science and social structure, health service and society* (Director General of Health Services of Norway, Oxford University Press, New York, 1960).

Freeman, R.B. and Holmes, Edward M. Jr., *Administration of Public Health Services* (Saunders, Philadelphia, 1960).

Frederick A. Praguer, *Community health services for New York City* (Commission on the Delivery of Personal Health Services, New York, 1969).

Friedlander, Walter, *Introduction to Social Welfare* (Prentice Hall, New York, 1955).

Gore, M.S., *Urbanization and the family change* (Popular Prakashan, Bombay, 1968).

Greer, Scott A., *Governing the metropolis* (Wiley, New York, 1962).

Grusky, Oscar, "*Role conflict in Organisation*", *Administrative Science Quarterly* (March, 1959).

Hall, Penilope M., *Social Services of Modern England* (Routledge and Kegan Paul Ltd., 1953).

Hamilton, James A., *Decision making in hospital administration and medical care,* a case book (Minnesote Press, Minneapolis, 1961).

Hanlon, John I., *Principles of Health Administration* (St. Louis, C.V. Mosby Company, 1963).

Hauser, P.M., *Hand book for social research in urban areas* (UNESCO, Paris, 1965).

Hill, R. et al., *Family and Population Control*, a Puerto Rican experiment in social change (University of North Carolina Press, 1959).

"*Urbanisation and Urban Development*", *The Indian Journal of Public Administration Vol. XIV, No. 3* (Indian Institute of Public Administration, 1968).

Jacl, E.G. ed., *Patients, physicians and illness*, a source book in behavioral science and medicine (Free Press of Glencoe, New York, 1964).

Jefferys, Margot, *An anatomy of social welfare services* (Michael Joseph, London, 1965).

Jagannadham, V. and Bakshi, N.S., *Citizen and Municipal Bureaucracy* (I.I.P.A., Delhi, 1971).

League of Nations, *Health Organisation in British India*, League of Nations, 1928.

Likert, Reusis, "*Measuring organisational performance*", *Harvard Business Review* (March & April, 1958).

Marsh, Novman H., "Strategy in administrative action", *Hospital Administration, Spring,* 1958.

Marsh, David C., *An introduction to the study of social administration* (London, Routledge and Kegan Paul, London, 1965).

Martain, Guinn and Alton, Baker, *Supervisor and his job* (McGraw Hill, New York, 1965).

Mitra, Asok, *Delhi Capital City* (Thompson Press (India) Ltd., New Delhi, 1970).

Moss, J., *Health and welfare services hand book* (3rd ed., Hadden Best & Co. Ltd., 1962).

Mumford, Emily and J.K. Skipper Jr., *Sociology in hospital care* (Harper & Row, New York, 1967).

Parson, Glenn, *Notes on administration of Delhi Province*, 1926.

Paul, B.D., *Health, Culture and Community*, case studies of public relations to health programme (Russell Sage Foundation, New York, 1964).

Parker, Julia, *Local Health and Welfare Services* (George Allen and Unwin, London, 1965).

Robson, William A., ed., *Great cities of the world, their government, politics and planning* (Allen & Unwin, London, 1954).

Rao, V.K.R.V. and Desai, P.B., *Greater Delhi*—a study in urbanisation, 1940-57 (Asia Publications, Bombay, 1965).

Ruck, S.K., *London Government and the Welfare Services* (Routledge and Kegan Paul, London, 1963).

Simmons, L.W. and Wolff, H.G., *Social Science in medicine*, (Russell Sage Foundation, New York, 1963).

Simon, Herbert A., *Administrative behaviour*, a study of the decision making process in administrative organisation (Macmillan, New York, 1957).

Smolensky, J. and Franklin, B. Har, *Principles of Community Health* (W.B. Saunders Co., New York, 1961).

Taylor, Carl E. and others, *The Health Centre doctor in India* (John Hopkins Press, Baltimore, 1967).

Tead Ordway, The art of administration (McGraw Hill, New York, 1951).

Tead Ordway, "Reflections on the art of administration" (*Hospital Administration*, Winter, 1959).

Titmuss, R.H., *Essays on Welfare State* (Allen and Unwin, London, 1958).

Thompson, James D., "*Organisational management of conflict*", Administrative Science Quarterly, March, 1960.

Towards a Measure Medical Care Operational Research in the Health Services (A symposium published for the Nuffield Provincial Hospital Trust by Oxford University Press, 1962).

Vasey, Wayne, *Government and Social Welfare,* roles of federal, state and local governments in administering welfare services (Reinhart, New York, 1959).

White, R. Clyde, *Administration of public welfare* (American Book Co., New York, 1950).

Winslow, C.E.A., *The cost of sickness and the price of health* (W.H.O., Geneva, 1951).

Reports and Documents

Central Family Planning Institute : *Workshop on training of family planning personnel,* March 8, 12, 1966—Report and recommendations (New Delhi, the Institute, 1967).

Corporation of Madras—Annual Administration Report 1967-68, Pt. 1.

Corporation of Calcutta, Annual Administration Report 1968-69.

Delhi State Medical and Health Reorganisation Enquiry Committee Report, Government of India, 1965.

Director General Health Services—*Report of the Hospital Equipment Standards Action Committee* (D.G.H.S., Govt. of India, 1964).

Gillabaud Committee Report on U.K. Health Services (H.M.S.O., London, 1954).

Health and Welfare, the Development of Community Care Plans for the health and welfare services of the Local Authorities in England and Wales (H.M.S.O., London, 1963).

India—Health Ministry—*Proceedings of the first/second meeting of the Family Planning Communication and Motivation Action Research Committee* (Annual Report 1967-68).

India—Health Ministry, *Report of the Health Survey and Planning Committee* (Manager of Publications, Delhi, 1962).

India—Planning Commission, *Programme Evaluation Organisation—Evaluation of the family planning programme in India* (Planning Commission, New Delhi, 1965).

India—Planning Commission, Committee on Plan Projects, *Report on general hospitals* (Planning Commission, New Delhi, 1964).

India—Committee on Plan Projects, *Report on collection and disposal of refuse* (New Delhi, 1964, cyclostyled).

India, Health Ministry, *Report of the Family Planning Orienta-tion Training Courses Committee* (New Delhi, the Ministry, 1963).

India—Health Survey and Development Committee-14 (Three Volumes) (Delhi, Manager of Publications, 1946).

India International Centre, *Report of the Seminar on social administration in developing countries* (New Delhi, The Centre, 1964).

India—Ministry of Health, *Report of the Integration of Health Services* (Govt. of India, 1966).

India—*Review on the Hospital Services in Delhi Committee Report*, Director General of Health Services, 1968 (Mimeo).

India—*Report of Health Survey and Planning Committee*, Vol. I and Vol. II, Ministry of Health, Govt. of India, 1962.

India—*Report on Rural-Urban Relationship Committee*, Vol. I, II & III—Govt. of India, 1967.

India—*Report of the Study Group on Hospitals* (Govt. of India, 1968).

Indian Institute of Public Administration, *The experience of citizens in getting water connections* (I.I.P.A., New Delhi, 1965).

Indian Institute of Public Administration, *Citizens grievances in development administration* (Mimeo) (I.I.P.A., New Delhi, 1967).

Indian Council of Medical Research, *Morbidity survey of Central Health Services beneficiaries in Delhi* (New Delhi, the Council, 1964).

Indian Institute of Public Administration, Science and Govt. Unit, Citizen and hospital administration, 3 parts (New Delhi, the Institute, 1970).

Municipal Corporation of Delhi, *A brief review of the Financial Position of the General Wing of the Corporation*, Town Hall, D.M.C., 1967.

Municipal Corporation of Delhi—Year Book 1969-70.

Municipal Corporation of Delhi—*Establishment Schedules*, D.M.C., Delhi, 1968, 1969, 1970.

Municipal Corporation of Delhi—*Annual Budget Report*, D.M.C., Delhi, 1960-70.

Members Guide for Delhi—Municipal Corporation officials 1970-71.

Municipal Corporation of Delhi—*Annual Reports*, D.M.C., Delhi, 1959-60, 1960-61, 1961-62, 1962-63 and 1963-64.

Report of the Committee on Local Authority and Allied Personal Social Services (Her Majesty's Stationery Office, London, 1968).

National Institute of Health Administration and Education, *Report and recommendations of the workshop on state level planning and evaluation of health and family planning* (New Delhi, The Institute, 1968—Cyclostyled).

United Kingdom—Health Ministry and Local Govt., Belfast, *Report on health and local government administration in Northern Ireland 1962-63* (H.M.S.O., London, 1967).

United Kingdom, *Report of the Committee on local authority and allied personal social services* (H.M.S.O., London, 1969).

United Kingdom, *Royal Commission on local government in England*, 1966-69, 3 volumes (H.M.S.O., London, 1969).

United Nations, United Nations Advisory Mission, *Report of the family planning programme in India* (U.N., New York, 1966).

United Nations : *Report of the Organisation and Administration of Social Service, 1962* (U.N., New York, 1962).

United States Department of Health, Education and Welfare, *Guidelines for hospital modernization, 1965.*

Appendices

Extract from the Bhore Committee Report on Health Administration of Delhi (Vol. V—Chapter III)

He strongly recommends that a single authority should be established for the health administration in Delhi Province as a whole. It may be designated as Delhi Provincial Health Board... Population of Delhi City is in far excess of 200,000 and the population of New Delhi is not far from this. Although we have recommended that municipalities of this size may be permitted to develop their own health organisations provided desired efficiency is maintained, we feel that the purpose of demonstration will be better served by merging these local bodies into a province-wide health authority by permitting them to maintain their separate health services with whatever safeguards Government may impose for promoting their efficiency. We feel that existence of two urban and one rural health authorities functioning independently in a province like Delhi must militate against development of an efficient integrated health service and must render difficult the formulation and execution of a unified health policy for the area as a whole.

Delhi Health Board should consist of representatives of local authorities and of representatives elected directly by people. At initial stage, Chief Commissioner should be chairman and later on giving way to elected chairman.

APPENDIX A.2

List of Hospitals in Delhi with distribution of beds as on 1.1.1967

Authority/Hospital	Type	Total No. of beds
A. Delhi Administration		
1. Irwin Hospital	General	1,068
2. G.B. Pant Hospital	General	258
3. Police Hospital	General	50
4. Poor House Hospital	General	30
5. Shahdara Mental Hospital	Special	400
B. Central Government		
1. Safdarjang Hospital	General	994
2. Willingdon Hospital	-do-	600
3. General Hospital Delhi Cantt	-do-	30
C. Statutory Body		
1. All India Institute of Medical Sciences, New Delhi	General	414
2. Lady Hardinge Medical College and Hospital	-do-	549
3. Kalavati Saran Children Hospital	Special	235
D. Indian Railway Authority		
1. Northern Railway Hospital Queens Road	General	70
2. Central Railway Hospital	-do-	130

E. Municipal Corporation (Urban)

1. S.J.T.B. Hospital Kingsway Camp	Special T.B.	1,113
2. Victoria Zanana Hospital	General	175
3. Balak Ram Hospital	-do-	20
4. Hindu Rao Hospital	-do-	227
5. I.D. Hospital Kingsway Camp	Special	117
6. Patel Nagar Hospital	General	15
7. Moti Nagar Hospital	-do-	15
8. Kalkaji Colony Hospital	-do-	15
9. Malviya Nagar Hospital	-do-	15
10. Lajpat Nagar Hospital	-do-	15
11. Tilak Nagar Hospital	-do-	15
12. Shahdara Civil Hospital	-do-	12
13. Shahdara General Hospital	-do-	50
14. Hudson Lines Maternity Hospital, Kingsway Camp	-do-	30
15. Mrs. Girdhari Lal Maternity Hospital	Special	97

F. Municipal Corporation (Rural)

1. Roop Ram Health Centre	General	15
2. Primary Health Centre	General	6
3. Primary Health Centre Mehrauli	-do-	12
4. Primary Health Centre Narela	-do-	10
5. Primary Health Centre Kathepur	-do-	6

G. Voluntary Organisations

1. R.K. Mission T.B. Clinic	Special	28
2. R.B. Seth Jessa Ram Hospital	General	53
3. Dr. Shroff Eye Hospital	Special	210
4. All-India Blind Relief Society	-do-	80

5. Tirath Ram Shah Hospital — General — 115
6. Sant Parmanand Blind Relief Mission — Special — 86
7. Delhi Maternity Hospital — General — 108
8. St. Stephen's Hospital — -do- — 221
9. Sir Ganga Ram Hospital — -do- — 122
10. Shyam Lal Free Eye Hospital — Special Eye — 20
11. Shri Mool Chand Khairati Ram Trust — General — 120
12. T.B. Hospital Mehrauli — Special — 306
13. New Delhi T.B. Centre — -do- — 15

H. New Delhi Municipal Committee

1. Moti Bagh Centre — General — 36
2. Lodhi Road Maternity Ward — Special — 12
3. Sarojini Nagar Maternity Ward — -do- — 12
4. Kitchner Road Maternity Ward — -do- — 13

APPENDIX A.3

Institutions under Health Department, M.C.D.

3.1 List of the Allopathic Hospitals/Dispensaries and Primary Health Centres

	Name of Institution	Beds
Major Hospitals	*1. S.J.T.B. Hospital† **	1,113
	*2. Hindu Rao Hospital† **	306
	*3. Victoria Zanana Hospital**	175
	*4. I.D. Hospital**	165
	*5. Mrs. G.L. Maternity Hospital**	97
	*6. General Hospital, Shahdara†	50
Colony Hospitals	*7. Tilak Nagar Hospital† **	47
	*8. Lajpat Nagar Hospital† **	47
	*9. Malviya Nagar Hospital	31
	*10. Moti Nagar Hospital**	31
	*11. Kalkaji Colony Hospital**	31
	*12. H.L. Maternity Hospital	30
	*13. Balak Ram Hospital**	25
	*14. Patel Nagar Hospital**	15
	*15. Civil Hospital, Shahdara**	12

Primary   16. Primary Health Centre, Mehrauli**   10
Health   *17. Primary Health Centre, Kanjhawla**   15
Centres *18. Primary Health Centre, Narela**   10
             *19. Primary Health Centre, Alipur**   6
             *20. Primary Health Centre, Fatehpur Beri**   6

                                                              2,223

Dispen- *21. Karol Bagh Dispensary
saries   *22. W.E.A. Urban Health Centre
             *23. Rajinder Nagar Dispensary
             *24. Jama Masjid Dispensary**
             *25. Lal Kuan Dispensary
             *26. Lahori Gate Dispensary**
             *27. Kashmere Gate Dispensary
             *28. Town Hall Dispensary
             *29. Bara Hindu Rao Dispensary
             *30. Sadar Bazar (Male) Dispensary
             *31. Sadar Bazar (Female) Dispensary
             *32. Paharganj Dispensary**
             *33. Jhil Khuranja Dispensary
             *34. Patpar Ganj Dispensary
             *35. New Tehar Dispensary
             *36. Ramesh Nagar Dispensary
             *37. Naraina Dispensary
             *38. Goenka Road Dispensary
             *39. Azadpur Dispensary**
             *40. Indra Nagar Dispensary
             *41. Jangpura Dispensary
              42. Bijwasan Dispensary
             *43. Daulat Pur Dispensary
              44. Shakur Basti Dispensary
              45. Badli Dispensary
              46. Urban Health Centre, Nimri
              47. Urban Health Centre, Outram Lines
              48. Bawana Dispensary
              49. Qutabgarh Dispensary
              50. Nangloi Dispensary
              51. Karala Dispensary

	*52. Madangir Khadar Dispensary
	*53. Badarpur Dispensary
	*54. Madangir Camp Dispensary
	*55. Urban Health Centre, Defence Colony
T.B.	*56. T.B. Clinic, S.P. Marg†
Clinics	*57. T.B. Clinic, Moti Nagar†
	*58. T.B. Clinic, Jhandewalan†
	*59. T.B. Clinic, Shahdara†
V.D.	60. V.D. Clinic, Jama Masjid
Clinics	61. V.D. Clinic, Roshanara Road
Leprosy	62. Leprosy Home, Tahirpur
Home	63. Leprosy Clinic, Jama Masjid
& Clinic	64. Mobile Dispensary No. 1
Mobile	65. Mobile Dispensary No. 2
Dispen-	66. Mobile Dispensary No. 3
saries	67. Mobile Dispensary No. 4
	68. Mobile Dispensary No. 5
	69. Mobile Dispensary No. 6
	70. Public Health Laboratory

*Anti-rabies treatment   **Ambulance services
†X-ray services

3.2 *List of Ayurvedic Dispensaries/Veterinary Dispensaries/ Hospitals/Vaccination Centres*

Ayurvedic	1. Ballimaran	
Hospital		
Ayurvedic	2. Andha Mughal	14. Jawahar Nagar
Dispensaries	3. Arya Pura	15. Karol Bagh
	4. Ashok Nagar	16. Katra Khushal Rai
	5. Bagh Kare Khan	17. Model Basti
	6. Bhogal	18. Moti Bagh
	7. Bazar Sita Ram	19. New Rajinder Nagar
	8. Chawla	20. Narain Dutta
	9. Darya Ganj	21. Pahari Dhiraj
	10. Azadpur	22. Pahar Ganj
	11. Double Phatak	23. Rohtas Nagar
	12. Seema Puri	24. Tri Nagar
	13. Gandhi Nagar	25. Seelampur

26.	Subzi Mandi	31.	Churiwalan
27.	Town Hall	32.	Kashmere Gate
28.	Teli Wara	33.	Kalan Masjid
29.	Halambi Khurd	34.	Narela
30.	Chandni Mahal	35.	Phatak Habash Khan
		36.	Mehrauli

Homoeopa- 37. Shahdara
thic Dispensaries

Pharmacy 1. Nigam Bodh Gate

Veterinary	1.	Tis Hazari	7.	Tihar
Hospitals	2.	Shahdara	8.	Alipur
	3.	Mehrauli	9.	Bawana
	4.	Bijwasan	10.	Narela
	5.	Dhansa	11.	Nangloi
	6.	Najafgarh		
Veterinary	12.	Badli	18.	Daulatpur
Dispensa-	13.	Karanwal Nagar	19.	Kutub Garh
ries	14.	Gitorni	20.	Prehlad Pur
	15.	Badarpur		
	16.	Palam		
	17.	Jharoda Kalan		

Vaccination-cum-birth and death registration centres

1. Shahdara Zonal Office, Shahdara.
2. Old Post Office Bldg., Main Road, Gandhi Nagar.
3. Bulward Road, near Dead House, Delhi.
4. E-73, Timarpur Govt. Quarters, Delhi.
5. Outram Lines, near S.I.'s Office, Delhi.
6. Double Storey Quarters, Vijay Nagar, Delhi.
7. Azadpur Municipal Colony, Delhi.
8. Aryapura, Delhi.
9. Roshanara Road (near Palace Cinema).
10. Ghantaghar (near Akhara), Delhi.
11. Roshanara Garden, Delhi.
12. Maurice Nagar, Delhi.
13. Kamla Nagar, Delhi.
14. Town Hall, Delhi.
15. Hamilton Road, Delhi.
16. Lal Kuan, Delhi.

17. Ballimaran, Delhi.
18. Jama Masjid Dispensary, Delhi.
19. Chandni Mahal, Delhi.
20. Faiz Bazar, Delhi.
21. Gandhi Market, Delhi.
22. Bazar Sita Ram, Delhi.
23. Gali No. 1, Multani Dhandha, Delhi.
24. Amrit Kaur Market, New Delhi.
25. Basti Harphool Singh, New Delhi.
26. Ahata Kidara, Delhi.
27. Bahadur Garh Road, Delhi. .
28. 31/2, Ashok Nagar, New Delhi.
29. Subhash Nagar Dispensary, New Delhi.
30. Main Bazar, Nangal Raya, New Delhi.
31. J.J. Colony, Arya Samaj Mandir, New Delhi.
32. Moti Nagar, New Delhi.
33. Ramesh Nagar, New Delhi.
34. Shakur Basti, New Delhi.
35. Narela Tower, Delhi.
36. Naraina, New Delhi.
37. Najafgarh, New Delhi.
38. Jangpura Road, New Delhi.
39. Lajpat Nagar Hospital, Lajpat Nagar, New Delhi.
40. Kotla Mubarakpur, New Delhi.
41. S.I.S. Office, Kalkaji, New Delhi.
42. Malviya Nagar, New Delhi.
43. Moti Bagh II, New Delhi.
44. Mehrauli, New Delhi.
45. Kishan Ganj, Delhi.
46. Anand Parbat, Delhi.
47. Karampura, Delhi.
48. Shanti Nagar, Delhi.
49. Bharat Nagar, Delhi.
50. South Patel Nagar, New Delhi.
51. West Patel Nagar, New Delhi.
52. Pusa Institute, New Delhi.
53. Chhapar Wala Kuan, New Delhi.
54. Gaffar Market, New Delhi.
55. Dev Nagar, New Delhi.

3.3 List of Maternity & Child Welfare, Family Planning Centres and Maternity Homes

1. Nicholson Road, Mori Gate, Delhi.
2. Dariba Kalan, adj. Jama Masjid Dispensary, Delhi.
3. F.P. Centre, Hindu Rao Hospital, Delhi.
4. Lahori Gate, opp. T.T. Post Dispensary Bldg., Delhi.
5. Katra Neel, Ch. Chowk, Delhi.
6. Kamra Bangash, Jama Masjid, Delhi.
7. Deshbandhu Gupta Road, Dispensary Bldg., Pahar Ganj, New Delhi.
8. Sarak Prem Narain, Churiwalan, Bazar Sita Ram, New Delhi.
9. Thompson Road, New Delhi.
10. A-30, Motia Khan, New Delhi.
11. Basti Harphool Singh, near Police Station, Sadar Bazar, Delhi.
12. Main Bazar, Teliwara, Delhi.
13. Pusa Institute, Pusa Road, New Delhi.
14. Patel Nagar Hospital, New Delhi.
15. Dev Nagar, Karol Bagh, New Delhi.
16. Gali No. 24, Naiwala, K. Bagh, New Delhi.
17. Bagh Kare Khan, Old Rohtak Road, New Delhi.
18. Model Basti, New Delhi.
19. 112-C, Timarpur, Delhi.
20. Khyber Pass, Delhi.
21. Hudson Lines, Kingsway Camp, Delhi.
22. Seth Tek Chand Mat. Centre, Shakti Nagar, Delhi.
23. Azadpur Municipal Colony, Delhi.
24. Dhaka Municipal Colony, Delhi.
25. Bunyad Manzil, Subzimandi (near Clock Tower), Delhi.
26. Malka Ganj, Delhi.
27. Badli Village, Delhi.
28. Moti Nagar Hospital Bldg., New Delhi.
29. Ramesh Nagar, adjoining Ramesh Nagar Dispensary, New Delhi.
30. Tihar No. I, Delhi.
31. Tihar No. II, Delhi.
32. Tilak Nagar Hospital Bldg., Tilak Nagar, New Delhi.

33. Tri Nagar, near Shakur Basti, New Delhi.
34. Mohammad Sarai, Shahdara, Delhi.
35. Patpar Ganj, Delhi.
36. Jhil Khuranja, Gandhi Nagar, Delhi.
37. Jangpura, near Church Road, New Delhi.
38. Lajpat Nagar Hospital Bldg., New Delhi.
39. Kalkaji Hospital Bldg., Kalkaji, New Delhi.
40. Malviya Nagar Hospital Bldg., Malviya Nagar.
41. Kotla Mubarakpur, New Delhi.
42. Nehru Nagar, New Delhi.
43. Andrews Ganj, opp. Defence Colony, New Delhi.
44. Moti Bagh II, New Delhi.
45. R.K. Puram, New Delhi.
46. Mehrauli (adjoining public health centre), Delhi.
47. Fateh Pur Beri, Delhi.
48. Tughlakabad Village, Delhi.
49. Madanpur Khadar, Delhi.
50. Shahbad, Daulatpur, Delhi.
51. Bawana Village.
52. Khanjawala, Delhi.
53. Narela, Delhi.
54. Nangloi, Delhi.
55. Seelampur Nai Basti, Delhi.
56. Bharat Nagar, Delhi.
57. J.J. Colony, Madangir, Delhi.
58. Main Market, Indra Nagar, Delhi.
59. Alipur, Delhi.
60. Victoria Zanana Hospital, Delhi.
61. Girdhari Lal Maternity Hospital, Delhi.
62. Gandhi Nagar, Delhi.
63. Jawahar Nagar, Delhi.
64. Rajinder Nagar, Delhi.
65. Darya Ganj, Ansari Road, Delhi.
66. Pahari Imli.

Sub-Centres

67. Vikram Nagar, Kotla Feroz Shah, Delhi.
68. Rana Pratap Bagh, Civil Lines, Delhi.
69. Ram Pura, New Delhi.

70. Nangal Rai, New Delhi.
71. Jhilmil Colony, B-102, Shahdara, Delhi.
72. Kutub Garh, Delhi.
73. Chirag Delhi.
74. Masjid Moth.
75. Shahpur Jatt, Delhi.
76. Sriniwaspuri, New Delhi.
77. Gitorni, Delhi.
78. Deoli, Delhi.
79. Badarpur, Delhi.
80. Asola, Delhi.
81. Jaun Pur, Delhi.
82. Nizam Pur, Delhi.
83. Libaspur, Delhi.
84. Khera Khurd, Delhi.
85. Makhmelpur, Delhi.
86. Prehladpur, Delhi.
87. Auchandi, Delhi.
88. Haidarpur, Delhi.
89. Burari, Delhi.
90. Mandka, Delhi.
91. Madipur, Delhi.
92. Hari Nagar, Delhi.
93. Geora, Delhi.
94. Khanjhawla Village, Delhi.
95. Dera, Delhi.
96. Chatter Pur, Delhi.
97. Puth Kala, Delhi.
98. Jaunti, Delhi.

Whole-time family planning centres

1. Chandni Chowk, Delhi.
2. Lahori Gate, Delhi.
3. Jama Masjid, Delhi.
4. Nicholson Road, Delhi.
5. Hauz Qazi, Delhi.
6. Sarak Prem Narain, Delhi.
7. Basti Harphool Singh, Delhi.
8. Pahar Ganj, New Delhi.

9. Teliwara, Delhi.
10. Motia Khan, New Delhi.
11. Jawala Nagar, Delhi.
12. Shakti Nagar, Delhi.
13. Timarpur, Delhi.
14. Kingsway Camp, Delhi.
15. Azadpur, Delhi.
16. Model Basti, Delhi.
17. Rajinder Nagar, New Delhi.
18. Patel Nagar, New Delhi.
19. Bagh Kare Khan, Delhi.
20. Moti Nagar, New Delhi.
21. Jangpura, New Delhi.
22. Lajpat Nagar, New Delhi.
23. Malviya Nagar, New Delhi.
24. Kalkaji, New Delhi.
25. Seelampur, Delhi.
26. Shahdara, Delhi.
27. Jhil Khuranja, Delhi.
28. Alipur, Delhi.
29. Narela, Delhi.
30. Mehrauli, Delhi.
31. Fatehpur Beri, Delhi.
32. G.L. Maternity Hospital, Delhi.
33. Victoria Zanana Hospital, Delhi.
34. Khanjawala, Delhi.

Maternity Homes

1. Maternity Home, Darya Ganj Street No. 1, Ansari Road, Delhi.
2. Maternity Home, Jawahar Nagar, Delhi.
3. Maternity Home, Old Rajinder Nagar, New Delhi.
4. Maternity Home, Pahari Dhiraj, Sadar Bazar, Delhi.
5. Maternity Home and Fondling Home, Shakti Nagar, near Nagiya Chowk, Delhi.

APPENDIX A.4

Progress of Family Welfare Planning Centres in respect of IUCD, sterilization and overall performance during Sept. 1968 in all agencies working within Union Territory of Delhi

Sl. No.	Name of the Agency	IUCD Insertions			Sterilization Operations			Overall Performance		
		Target	Achieve- ment	% of Target achieved	Target	Achieve- ment	% of Target achieved	Target	Achieve- ment	% of Target achieved
1.	M.C.D.	680	659	96.9	1,020	334	32.7	1,360	920	67.6
2.	D.G.H.S.	60	47	78.3	90	107	118.9	117	268	229.1
3.	C.G.H.S.	280	142	50.7	420	83	19.8	560	2,080	371.4
4.	Safdarjang Hospital	20	6	30.0	30	66	220.0	40	108	270.0
5.	A.I.I.M.S.	20	22	110.0	30	19	63.3	40	63	157.5
6.	Lady Hardinge Hospital	20	1	5.0	30	13	43.3	40	39	97.5
7.	Tibbia College	20	—	—	30	5	16.7	40	5	12.5
8.	Irwin Hospital	20	45	225.0	30	116	386.6	40	179	447.5
9.	N.D.M.C.	80	13	16.3	120	48	40.0	160	220	137.5
10.	CG Hospital (Cantt Board)	20	16	80.0	30	7	23.3	40	40	100.0
11.	Andhra Vanitha Mandli	20	3	15.0	30	5	16.7	40	15	37.5
12.	N.D.F.P.A.	20	7	35.0	30	44	146.7	40	367	917.5
13.	Delhi Medical Association	20	2	10.0	30	1	—	40	17	42.5
14.	Delhi U. Women Asson.	10	13	130.0	15	1	6.7	20	21	105.0
15.	Jessa Ram Hospital	20	14	70.0	30	28	93.3	40	37	92.5

	20	7	30	35.0	71	236.7	40	129	322.5
16. Ganga Ram Hospital	20	7	30	35.0	71	236.7	40	129	322.5
17. Delhi Maternity Hospital	20	3	30	15.0	38	126.7	40	86	215.0
18. Tirath Ram Hospital	20	8	30	40.0	25	83.0	40	72	180.0
19. St. Stephen's Hospital	20	14	30	70.0	18	60.0	40	45	112.5
20. Hamdard Clinic	20	—	30	—	12	40.0	40	29	72.5
21. Rotary Club, Madangir	20	7	30	35.0	4	13.3	40	19	47.5
22. Others	20	8	—	40.0	21	—	—	165	—
Total :	1,290	1,037	1,940	80.4	1,065	54.9	2,530	4,940	195.3

Designation, scale of pay and nature of appointment of the senior officials of the Health Department of the Corporation as on 1969*

Category of Staff	Designation	Pay Scale above Rs. 350	Nature of appointment	
			Permanent	Temporary
Public Health A—Gerneral Supervision Establishment	Municipal Health Officer	1300-60-1600-100-1800 +Rs. 250/- fixed P.M.	1	—
	Deputy Health Officer (P.H.)	700-40-1100-50/2 1250	1	—
	Zonal Health Officer	375-25-500-30-590-EB-30-800-EB-30-830-35-900+NPA	7	—
	Administrative Officer (H)	350-25-500-30-590-EB-30-800-EB-30-830-35-900	1	—
	Assistant Chief Accountant (H)	—do—	1	—
Epidemics Epidemic Investigation Bureau	Epidemiologist	675-35-850-40-1050-50-1300 +NPA	—	1
Malaria & Insecticides	Dy. Health Officer (Malaria)	700-40-1100-50/2-1250+125 as C.A.	1	—
Miscellaneous	Public Analyst	375-25-500-30-590-	1	—

* The pay-scale has since been revised with the recommendation of Third Pay Commission, 1974.

(i) Laboratory		EB-30-800-EB-30-830-35-900		
	Assistant Health Officer (Food)	—do—	1	—
Medical Relief A. General	D.H.O. (Medical)	700-40-1100-50/2-1250	1	—
	D.H.O. (M & CW)	—do—	1	—
	A.H.O. (Pl/Med.)	375-25-500-30-590-EB-30-800-EB-30-830-35-900	1	—
Hospitals, Maternity Homes & Clinics	1. Medical Superintendent	1150-50-1500	1	—
	2. Physician	700-40-1100-50/2-1250	1	—
Hindu Rao Hospital	3. Children Specialist	—do—	1	—
	4. Medical Specialist	—do—	1	—
	5. Psychiatrist	—do—	1	—
	6. Orth. Surgeon	—do—	1	—
	7. Senior Anaesthetist	—do—	1	—
	8. Sr. Radiologist	—do—	1	—
	9. Physician/Surgeon	—do—	1	—
	10. Obstetrician	—do—	1	—
	11. ENT Specialist	—do—	1	—
	12. Ophthalmologist	—do—	1	—
	13. Anaesthetist	375-25-500-30-590-EB-30-800-EB-30-830-35-900	1	—
	14. Junior Radiologist	—do—	1	—
	15. Skin & V.D. Specialist	—do—	1	—
	16. Junior Pathologist	—do—	1	—
	17. Dental Surgeon	—do—	1	—
	18. Matron	390-20-450-25-475	1	—
	19. Pathologist	700-40-1100-50/2-1250	—	1
	20. Blood Transfusion Officer	375-25-500-30-590-EB-30-800-EB-30-830-35-900	—	1
S.J.T.B. Hospital	1. Medical Superintendent	1150-50-1500	1	—
	2. Thoracic Surgeon	700-40-1100-50/2-1250	1	—

	3. Chest Physician	—do—	1	—
	4. Radiologist	—do—	1	—
	5. Deputy Medical Superintendent	375-25-500-30-590-EB-30-800-EB-30-830-35-900	1	—
	6. Anaesthetist	—do—	1	—
	7. Junior Medical Officer	—do—	1	—
	8. Pathologist	—do—	1	—
	9. Matron	390-20-450-25-475	1	—
Victoria Zanana Hospital	1. Medical Superintendent	700-40-1100-50/2-1250	1	—
	2. Matron	390-20-450-25-475	1	—
	3. Anaesthetist	375-25-500-30-590-EB-30-800-EB-30-830-35-900	1	—
	4. Resident Medical Officer	—do—	2	—
	5. Radiologist	—do—	1	—
	6. Physician	—do—	1	—
	7. Paediatrician	—do—	1	—
Balak Ram Hospital	1. Medical Superintendent	—do—	1	—
Hospitals in colonies of displaced persons	1. Medical Superintendent	—do—	2	—
Mrs. Girdhari Lal Maternity Hospital	1. Resident Superintendent	—do—	1	—
	2. Anaesthetist	—do—	1	—
I.D. Hospital	1. Medical Superintendent	675-35-850-40-1050-50-1300+NPA	1	—
	2. Pathologist	675-25-850-40-1050-50-1300	1	—
	3. Matron	390-20-450-25-475	1	—
	4. Dy. Medical Superintendent	375-25-500-30-590-EB-30-800-EB-30-830-35-900	1	—
	5. Junior Physician	—do—	1	—
Ayurvedic Hospital	1. Resident Superintendent	425-25-450-30-600-35-705-EB-35-950+NPA	1	—
Tuberculosis Clinics	1. Senior Medical Officer	570-30-600-35-670-EB-35-950+NPA	1	—
T.B. Clinic S.P. Mukerji Marg	1. Senior Medical Officer	375-25-500-30-590-EB-30-800-EB-30-	—	1

T.B. Clinic Shahdara		830-35-900		
T.B. Clinic Moti Nagar	1. Senior Medical Officer	375-25-500-30-590-EB-30-800-EB-30 830-35-900 Personal grade of present incumbent 425-25-450-30-600 35-705-EB-35-950 +NPA	—	1
T.B. Clinic Jhandewalan	1. Senior Medical Officer	375-25-500-30-590-EB-30-800-EB-30-830-35-900+NPA	1	—
M & CW Centres and Homes	1. Cas Grade I	375-25-500-30-590-EB-30-800-EB-30-830-35-900+NPA	1	—
Genl. Hospital Shahdara	1. Med. Superin-tendent	700-40-1100-50/2-1250	—	1
	2. Senior Surgeon	—do—	—	1
	3. Jr. Ophthalmo-logist	375-25-500-30-590-EB-30-800-EB-30-830-35-900+NPA	—	1
	4. Jr. Anaesthetist	—do—	—	1
	5. Jr. Gynaecolo-gist/Obstetrician	—do—	—	1
	6. Jr. Radiologist	—do—	—	1
	7. Jr. Pathologist	—do—	—	1
	8. Jr. ENT Surgeon	—do—	—	1
	9. Jr. Physician	—do—	—	1
	10. Matron	390-20-450-25-475	—	1
C. Dispensary (a) Allopathic Dispensary	1. Bacteriologist	375-25-500-30-590-EB-30-800-EB-30-830-35-900	1	—
Ayurvedic Homoeopathic and Unani Dispensaries	1. D.H.O I.S.M.	675-35-850-40-1050-50-1300+Car All. & Rs. 200 NPA	1	—
	2. Officer I/C Pharmacy Store	425-25-450-30-600-35-705-EB-35-950 +NPA	1	—

APPENDIX B.2

Table showing allocation of staff in Colony Hospitals, M.C.D. during 1968-69

Name of institution & concerned zone	Res. Supdt.	CAS Gr I	UDC	LDC	S/ Nurse	Dis-penser	Dre-sser	Lab. Asstt	Mid-wife	Dri-ver	Dental Surgeon	D/ Tech	X-Ray Asstt	D.R. Asstt	N/ ord	Dai	T. Class IV
Lajpat Nagar Hosp.	1	3	1	2	6	4	1	1	2	1	1	1	1	1	1	—	21
Tilak Nagar Hosp.	1	3	1	2	5	4	1	1	2	1	—	—	1	1	1	—	18
Patel Nagar Hosp.	—	2	1	1	1	2	1	1	1	1	1	—	—	—	—	—	12
Moti Nagar Hosp.	—	3	1	1	4	3	1	1	1	1	1	1	—	—	—	—	20
Kalkaji Colony Hosp.	—	3	1	1	3	3	1	1	1	1	—	—	—	—	—	—	17
Malviya Nagar Hosp.	—	3	1	1	3	3	1	1	—	1	—	—	—	—	—	—	17
G.L. Maty. Hosp.	—	3	1	1	3	3	2	1	1	—	—	—	—	—	—	—	14
Dental Staff R. Zone	—	—	—	—	1	—	—	—	—	—	1	1	—	—	—	—	2
Dental Staff Shahdara	—	—	—	—	1	—	—	—	—	—	1	1	—	—	—	—	2
Total staff :	2	20	7	9	27	22	8	7	8	6	4	4	2	2	2	—	123

APPENDIX B.3

Table showing zone-wise allocation of staff of Vety. Hospitals & Dispensaries in Health Department, M.C.D.

Name of Institu-tion	Vety. Compounder Stock Asstt.	LDC	Dres-ser	Class IV	P.T. Chow-kidar
Shahdara Zone					
Vety. Hospital Shahdara	1+1	—	1	1+1	—
O.L.D. Karwal Nagar	1	—	—	2	—
New Delhi South Zone					
Vety. Hospital Mehrauli	2	—	1	2	—
Vety. Dispensary Ghitorni	1	—	—	2	—
Vety. Dispensary Tikri Kalan	1	—	—	2	—
Vety. Dispensary Badarpur	1	—	1	2	—
Civil Lines Zone					
Vety. Hospital Tis Hazari	2	—	—	8	—
West Zone					
Vety. Hospital New Tehar	1	—	—	2	—
D.H.O. (Medical) Office					
D.H.O. (MED) Office	—	1	—	—	—
Rural Zone					
Vety. Hospital Tikri Kalan	1	—	—	2	—
Vety. Hospital Badli	1	—	—	2	—
Vety. Hospital Palam	1	—	—	2	—
Vety. Dispensary Daulatpur	1	—	1	2	1
Vety. Hospital Bijwasan	2	—	—	2	—

Vety. Hospital Dhansa	2	—	—	2	—
Vety. Hospital Najafgarh	2	—	—	2	—
O.L.D. Jharoda	1	—	—	2	—
O.L.D. Qutab Garh	1	—	1	2	1
O.L.D. Pahladpur	1	—	—	2	—
Vety. Hospital Alipur	2	—	—	2	—
O.L.D. Narela	1	—	—	2	—
Vety. Hospital Bawana	2	—	—	2	1
Vety. Hospital Nangloi	2	—	1	2	—
Total :	30	1	6	48	3

APPENDIX B.4

Table showing zone-wise allocation of staff of Allopathic Dispensaries

Name of Dispensary	CAS Gr I	Nurse M/Wife B.Gr.	Dres-ser	Dri-ver	Mid-wife	Class IV	P.T. Class IV	T. Dai	P.H. Nurse	Dispen-ser
Headquarters Staff										
1. H.Q. (Leave Reserve staff)	8									
2. M.D. No. 5	1	—	1	—	—	—	—	—	—	—
3. U.H.C. Outram Lines	—	—	—	—	—	2	—	—	—	—
City North Zone										
1. Town Hall Disp.	2	—	2	—	—	1	—	—	—	2
2. Kashmere Gate Disp	2	—	—	—	1	2	—	—	—	5
3. Lahori Gate Disp.	2	—	—	—	1	2	—	—	—	4
4. Lal Kuan Disp.	2	—	—	—	1	2	—	—	—	5
5. Jama Masjid Disp.	2	—	—	—	1	6	—	—	—	7
Karol Bagh Zone										
1. Dev Nagar Disp.	1	1	2	—	—	3	—	—	—	2
2. Rajinder Nagar Dispensary	1	—	1	—	—	3	—	—	—	3

Dispensary								
Shahdara Zone								
3. Naraina Disp.	1	—	1	—	2	—	1	1
4. U.H.C. W.E.A. Disp.	2	1	1	—	6	—	1	3
5. U.H.C. Nimri Disp.	2	1	1	—	6	—	1	3
Sadar Paharganj Zone								
1. Patparganj Disp.	1	—	1	—	2	—	1	1
2. Jhil Kuranja ,,	1	—	1	1	2	1	1	1
3. Mobile Disp. II	1	—	1	—	1	—	1	1
West Zone								
1. B.H.R. Disp.	2	—	2	—	2	1	1	5
2. S.B (F) ,,	1	1	1	1	4	—	1	2
3. S.B. (M) ,,	2	—	2	—	2	—	1	4
4. Paharganj ,,	2	—	2	—	2	1	1	4
1. Ramesh Nagar Disp.	1	—	1	—	3	—	1	1
2. New Tehar Disp.	1	—	1	—	2	—	1	2
3. Shakurbasti ,,	1	—	1	1	2	—	1	1
4. Mobile No. VI	1	—	1	—	1	1	1	1

Note : No provision for L.H.V., Vaccinator, Sanitary Inspector, Staff Nurse, U.D.C., Store Keeper or Lab. Asstt.

APPENDIX B.5

Table showing zone-wise distribution of the staff of Anti-malaria Operations during 1968-69

Designation	Shahdara Zone	C.L. Zone	City North Zone	City South Zone	S.P. Zone	K.B. Zone	West Zone	NDS Zone	Rural North	H.Q.	Total strength
1. Dy. Health Officer (Mal.)	—	—	—	—	—	—	—	—	—	1	1
2. Mal. Assistants	—	—	—	—	1	1	—	—	—	—	2
3. Insect Collectors	—	—	—	—	—	—	—	—	—	15	15
4. Malaria Jamadars	2	7	1	1	1	3	3	7	—	8	33
5. Malaria Beldars & Class IV	8	34	5	6	5	19	18	44	2	57	198
6. U.D. Clerks	—	—	—	—	—	—	—	—	—	1	1
7. Stenographers	—	—	—	—	—	—	—	—	—	1	1
8. L.D. Clerks	—	—	—	—	—	—	—	—	—	3	3
9. Driver	—	—	—	—	—	—	—	—	—	1	1

C.L. = Civil Lines
S.P. = Sadar Pahar Ganj
K.B.= Karol Bagh
N.D.S.=New Delhi South

APPENDIX B.6

Zone-wise Allocation of Budget for Medical Care in 1968-69

(in rupees)

Head of Account	Shahdara Zone	City North Zone	Civil Lines	S.P. Zone	K.B. Zone	West Zone	N.D. South Zone	Rural Zone	P.H. Lab.	D.H.O. (M&CW)	Head-quarters	Total Budget Estimates
1. Estt. & Decreetal charges	98800	245500	150500	153500	175000	97500	277500	473500	45000	55000	1633700	3410000
2. Contg.	3150	11160	6650	4170	5050	4660	10200	22260	10000	4000	35700	56000
3. Supply of Blood	—	—	—	—	—	—	—	—	—	—	5000	5000
4. Medicines	2000	4000	4000	3000	3000	3000	8000	12000	13000	—	1192000	1244000
5. Diets	—	—	—	—	—	250	500	3250	—	—	—	4000
6. Equip. & Apparatus	—	—	—	—	—	—	—	—	—	—	—	—
7. Ad hoc provision for opening of new Ayurvedic and Allopathic Dispensa-												

ries	—	—	—	—	—	—	—	—	250000	250000
8. Purchase of Mobile Van	—	—	—	—	—	—	—	—	100000	100000
9. Feed of animals	—	—	6000	—	—	—	—	—	—	6000
10. Stores	1000	2000	—	—	2000	8000	1000	—	2000	27100
11. Medical treatment of Mpl. Employees	—	—	—	—	—	—	—	—	—	—
	150000	—	—	—	—	—	—	—	150000	300000

Estt. : Establishment
Source : Corporation files

SCHEDULE 'A'

Interview Schedule for Administrators of the Health Department, Delhi Municipal Corporation, Delhi

Name of the Official
Section

Legislation

1. What are the bye-laws and acts governing the activities in your Department?

2. Which way your department is responsible for implementation of the provisions of D.M.C. Act 1958 and other health legislation in the State?

3. (a) Are all provisions of obligatory and compulsory duties relating to Municipal Corporation implemented throughout the Corporation area?   Yes/No.

    (b) If no, please state why?

4. (a) What are the difficulties (if any) do you think you face in implementation of the provisions of Corporation Act or bye-law on health provision?

    (b) What are your suggestions to eliminate these difficulties?

5. What do you think, are the drawbacks (if any) in the existing Corporation Act, for effective implementation of the health programme?

(a), (b), (c) and (d).

6. (a) Do you think the present procedure or system of Zonal decentralisation is effective procedure in getting the implementation of the health provisions of the Act?

Yes/No.

(b) If no, what are the difficulties in Zonal decentralisation?

(c) What further step and procedure do you suggest for efficient implementation of the programme, envisaged in the Act?

7. Is the procedure of medical stores adequate to obtain proper supply in time?

Rule making

8. Who makes the rules and regulations in regard to the management of the health department in the Corporation?

(1) State Government; (2) Commissioner;

(3) Standing Committee; (4) Corporation;

(5) Health Committee; (6) Health Officer.

9. What are the procedures of rule making?

10. How could changes be brought in the rule?

11. Do the voluntary organisations or the department concerned have any say in making of the rule?

12. Do you think that the persons who are responsible to implement these rules and regulations and bye-laws take part in making them?

13. If no, how does he express his dissatisfaction over the existing rule?

14. (a) Do you think of any rule and regulation standing in the way of effective implementation of the programme?

(b) If yes, give some examples.

15. Do you have any procedure to evaluate the effectiveness of the programme implemented?

16. Do you have similar rules and regulations for all the institutions working under this department?

17. *Health Committee Management*

(1) Do you have a Committee to advise on medical and public health problems?

(2) What is the constitution of the Committee? Who are the Members?

(3) To what extent Committee members attend meetings regularly and promptly?

(4) To what extent the Committee members participate in the discussions and decision making process?

(give example).

(5) To what extent Committee members show an understanding of the issues and problems presented?

(6) To what extent does the Committee member make contributions out of his experience?

(7) Do the Committee members keep the discussion impersonal and directed to the issues rather than to personalities?   (Yes/No.)   (If 'yes', specify.)

Organisation

(1) What are your functions?
   (a) with regard to the health department;
   (b) with regard to independent section.

(2) Is there any written policy or objective of the Health Department or for voluntary organisations?

(3) (a) Are you satisfied on the number of health dispensaries, hospitals and other services available in the Corporation?   Yes/No.

   (b) If 'no', do you like to have new institutions established under Corporation?

   (c) Do you recommend to bring private practitioners and voluntary organisations to provide the services?

   (d) Do you feel that the existing structure of the Health Department provides enough cooperation?

Yes/No.

If 'no', do you suggest any further change?

Coordination

1. Is there close cooperation among all the units of your department?

2. What is your relationship with other departments dealing with water supply, sewage disposal, Urban Community

Development, Housing and Slum Clearance in the Corporation?

3. Do you enlist cooperation of the voluntary organisations in Delhi engaged in family planning or other health services?

4. Is there any periodic meeting of the heads of all Sections of your department?   Yes/No.
If 'yes', what is the nature and purpose of such meeting?
How often do they meet?

5. How do you keep yourself informed about the activities and programmes of other departments engaged in health or other allied services?

6. Does the organisational structure provide enough opportunity for effective coordination among all units of the Department?

Personnel

1. (a) Is there any written law or regulation to cover personnel policy?   Yes/No.
   (b) If 'yes', are they followed properly?
   (c) If they are not followed, give some examples.
2. Is there a written job description for each position?
3. Are employees employed to specific positions with written job chart and duties attached to the post?
4. Do you consider staff development programme essential for your Department?
5. Is there any programme for staff development in your Department?   Yes/No.
   What facilities are provided?
   If not, what are the causes?
6. Do you consider that the salary, status and other conditions of service of your department are comparable to other government organisations in Delhi and do they attract qualified person to work in your Department?   Yes/No.
If 'no', have you taken any step to remove the difficulty?
1. What are the procedures followed in appointing staff in your department?
   (a) (1) Doctors, (2) Nurses, (3) Paramedicals, (4) Sweepers,
       (5) Social workers, family planning workers, extension

educators, (6) Midwives and lady health visitors, (7) Clerks and administrative staff.

(b) What are the requisite qualifications for the above posts?

2. Is there any scope for promotion of staff within the Organisation?

3. How long does it take one to get confirmed to a post?

4. (a) Are there recruiting problems for certain categories of job? Yes/No.

    (b) If 'yes', what are the causes?

    (c) How could they be alleviated?

5. What are the criteria governing promotion of staff in the Department—

    (a) Seniority, (b) Record of service,

    (c) Political pull, (d) any other (please specify).

6. How often and on what grounds the staff members are transferred?

    (a) Are there evidences of overstaffing and understaffing? Yes/No.

    (b) If 'yes', what are the causes?

7. Do you have arrangement of discussing problems with your staff?

8. What special benefits, other than pay, are given to the staff?

    (1) staff quarter, (2) welfare programme,

    (3) pension, provident fund, (4) any other.

9. Do you have any kind of job training for the staff?

Control and management and supervision

1. How do you control the activities of all institutions working under your section/department?

2. (a) Do you issue instructions from time to time?

    (b) Do you ask for reports from the institutions?

    (c) Do you ask the head of the institution to visit your office at regular intervals?

    (d) Do you pay visit to the institution for inspection?

    (e) Do you have any inspectorial staff to visit the field services?

3. Do you follow any procedure or proforma as an aid for your inspectional visit?

4. (a) Who or which officers inspect the institution?

   (b) What is the frequency of such inspection?

   (c) Do they inspect singly or in team?

   (d) Are the officers (food adulteration squad etc.) granted considerable power to decide the matter on the spot? Yes/No.

   (e) If 'no', has any attempt been made to correct the inadequacies pointed out by them?

   (f) How long does it take to decide the matter to put things right?

5. (a) Do you pay surprise visit to the institutions for inspection or visit on their request?

   Surprise visit/request visit

   (b) Do you think surprise visits are necessary?

6. While on inspection, do you supervise, direct or help the doctor in charge of the hospital/dispensary or H.C.H. Centre in their work? Yes/No.

If 'yes', give example as to how you help?

Do you or your officer meet the junior staff in informal meetings and help them with sorting out their day to day problems? Yes/No.

If 'yes', how often do you meet?

Do you have any system of listening to the grievances of the staff working under you? Yes/No.

If 'yes', are you in a position to redress their grievances and solve their problems? Yes/No.

If 'no', what are the impediments?

Finance

1. What are the major sources of funds in your Organisation?

Government grant, internal resources, public contribution.

2. What are the procedures of framing the budget for your department?

3. Are you satisfied with the budget formulation procedure of your organisation?

4. Do you have any say in budget allocation?

5. Do you think the finance for health services in Delhi Municipal Corporation is adequate?

6. What are the criteria of allocating funds?

7. Is there a uniform criterion for allocation of funds?

    (a) Are supplies adequate?

    (b) Are they made according to plan?

8. What is the criterion of providing grant-in-aid to the voluntary organisations?

9. Are you satisfied with the criteria adhered to?

10. Is there equitable distribution of resources in all areas of Delhi as per need or population basis?

Reports

How often do you receive reports from all your institutions?

Do you publish annual reports for all the services performed by the department?

What action do you take to inform public about your activities and the different procedures to obtain your services?

Public Relations

Do you have any written policy about public relations?

Do you provide any training in public relations to your staff?

Are you satisfied about public cooperation in relation to health department functioning?   Yes/No.

If 'no', why 'no', give causes.

Do you entertain the public complaints about the working of your department?   Yes/No.

If 'no', why?

Do you suggest any other way to enlist better public cooperation and improve public relations?

Evaluation

1. Is there a research or statistical wing in your Organisation?   Yes/No.

If 'yes', give details of their activities.

2. Are you satisfied with the performance of statistics section of your Department?   Yes/No.

If 'no', what improvement do you suggest?

3. Do you feel the need to make an occasional survey of the extent of health problem in Delhi to suggest the policy maker about the problem and bring about improvement?

4. Do you have any criteria to evaluate the performance of your department?   Yes/No.

If 'no', do you not feel the need to have it?

SCHEDULE 'B'

Interview Schedule for doctors in hospital, zonal headquarters, dispensaries and health centres, Health Department, M.C.D.

1. Name of the Institution.
2. Date of establishment.
3. Jurisdiction
   (a) area covered by the institution
   (b) types of specialised services rendered by the institution.

Legislation

1. (a) Do you think that the health provisions of the Delhi Municipal Corporation Act 1958 and the Bye-laws Bill 1965 are being implemented by your institution?
   (b) What are the difficulties, if any, in the way of effective implementation of the Act?
   (c) What measures do you suggest to remove these difficulties?

2. Do you think that the present procedure of supply of medical stores and medicines are effective? Yes/No.

If 'no', please state the difficulties of the present procedure.

3. (a) Do you think that the present procedure of punishing individual through fine is effective to implement public health standard? Yes/No.
   (b) If 'no', what is your suggestion? If 'yes', what are the difficulties in the Act? Please indicate measures to improve the present legal action for effective implementation.

Rule Making

1. Do you have any participation in framing the rules and regulations for the management of your institution?

2. Are you satisfied with the existing rules and regulations? Yes/No.

If not, how do you express your dissatisfaction?

3. Did you any time make any suggestion about any programme or scheme?

If 'yes', give instances.

Did you find favourable response/no response/no acknowledgement even?

4. Is there any method to evaluate the effectiveness of the rule to provide services?

5. Do you strictly follow the rules and regulations prescribed or you make certain modifications?

Follow the rule.

Make changes.

    (a) Who makes decision about the programmes in your institution?

    (b) Have you ever made suggestions about these programmes in consultation with your subordinates?

1. Does your system provide enough flexibility to adapt operational programme of your service to the requirements of the beneficiaries?

2. Do you feel that the medicine, finance, equipment and accommodation are sufficient to meet the needs of your clients? Yes/No.

If 'no', how the situation can be improved?

3. Do you think you have enough scope for your professional betterment and development in the institution?

4. Does the rule give you enough scope to utilise the authority at your level? Yes/No.

If 'yes', do you exercise them effectively?

Coordination

1. How far the employees of your institution have knowledge of other organisations?

2. How far other institutions are aware of your programme?

1. (a) Is there any kind of conflict or tension between the
       heads of different programmes in your institution?
       Yes/No.
   (b) If yes, what are the causes of conflict?
   (c) What steps do you suggest to bring about such
       cooperation?

2. Do you often meet the head of any other institution and
discuss your problem with him?

3. What is your staff members' reaction to voluntary organisations working in the area?

4. (a) Do you arrange occasional staff meetings? Yes/
       No.
   (b) If yes, what is the nature and purpose of such
       meetings?
   (c) Do the staff members express their views freely and
       frankly?
   (d) Do you take action on the suggestions made in these
       meetings?

Personnel

1. Is your institution covered by the personnel policy of
the Corporation?

2. Is there a written job description for each position?

3. Are employees appointed with specific duties and defined
conditions of service? Yes/No.

If yes, please furnish the copies of the duties.

Is there a personnel agency system to look after the
conditions of service of the employees? Yes/No.

If yes, what are their specific duties and functions?

1. Do you think that the salary and other conditions of
service in your institution are comparable to other similar
institutions?

What do you think the salary scales should be?

               (Please specify for each post)

2. Are there instances of employees leaving your institution? Yes/No.

If yes, please state the circumstances.

3. Are there scope and opportunities for promotion of
personnel in your institution?

4. What are the criteria governing promotion of staff in your institution?
  (a) Seniority
  (b) Record of Service
  (c) Additional professional qualification
  (d) Any other.

5. How often the members of the staff are transferred?

6. Are you consulted at the time of transfer and posting of staff in your institution?

7. What difficulties do you meet due to frequent transfer of your employees?

What suggestions would you make to improve the situation?

1. Are there any posts lying vacant in your institution at present? Yes/No.

If yes, what are the positions lying vacant, and why?

Does your institution provide any facility for staff development?

Management

  (a) Is there any advisory council at the Corporation level to manage your affairs? Yes/No.
  (b) If yes, what are their functions?
  (c) How often do they meet?
  (d) What are their powers?

1. Do you think you have enough freedom to decide your own affairs? Yes/No.

What difficulties are faced by want of freedom?

2. Do you think that your institution is understaffed? Yes/No.

If yes, what more staff is needed?

3. (a) Is there enough discipline among the members of the staff in your institution? Yes/No.
  (b) If not, what steps do you suggest to bring the discipline?

Supervision and Control

How do you check whether everything is being implemented

according to routine as it should be?

What do you do if your instructions are not followed by some of your subordinates?

How frequently do you inspect each unit/room of your institution?

Do you delegate your power to some of your subordinates? Yes/No.

(a) If yes, what powers have you delegated?

(b) When have you delegated the power?

Do you have authority to take disciplinary action against any of your subordinates? Yes/No.

(a) If yes, what type of action can you take?

(b) If no, what is the procedure in case you recommend disciplinary action against someone?

(c) Is the procedure effective enough to exercise control? Yes/No.

1. Does anybody from head office inspect your institution? Yes/No.

(a) If yes, who are they?

(b) How often do they inspect the institution?

2. To what aspect of management officers confine their inspection?

(a) *Quantitative aspect or physical standard*

(1) cleanliness, sanitation
(2) diet, if any
(3) furniture
(4) medical case record
(5) medical stores
(6) attendance of staff
(7) accommodation
(8) if anything other.

(b) *Guidance*

(1) Techniques of inservice training to new recruits.
(2) Development of training material.
(3) Development of health education material and techniques.
(4) Methods and use of record keeping (diary maintenance).

(5) How to treat a case through professional knowledge?

(6) Financial matters.

Do you or any of your subordinates direct or help?

Do you have time to

(a) direct or help the heads of different units of your institution? Yes/No.

(b) If no, state the reasons.

(1) Do you ever teach your subordinates on public relations, as to how to deal with public?

(2) How do you help your subordinates to improve their ability?

(FOR FAMILY PLANNING OFFICERS ONLY)

1. How many extension educators and health visitors are working under you?

(a) Do you periodically check their work?

(b) What procedure do you adopt to check that their entries in diary are correct?

(c) Do you give any instruction about their work? Yes/No.

(d) Do you feel quite satisfied about the manner of your inspection? Yes/No.

Finance

1. Are you satisfied with the financial procedure of securing funds from the Town Hall?

2. Do you have enough imprest amount in hand to cover emergency?

3. What are the bases of allocation of funds of your institution?

(a) Based on prorata share of the total cost of operating the institution.

(b) Based on per capita payment.

(c) Based on lumpsum grant.

(d) Others.

4. Who allocates resources in your institution?

(a) You with the help of your staff.

(b) Your parent Department in Health Department, Town Hall.

(c) Any other.

5. Do you have any participation in budget making process of the Corporation in allocation of funds for your institution? Yes/No.

6. Is there proper periodic auditing of accounts made to ensure proper utilisation of funds?

1. Did you have any occasion where the allotted amount could not be spent due to the procedural difficulty? (Give example, if any.)

2. Do you advocate charging fees from the beneficiaries?

3. Are you satisfied with the manner in which funds are allocated to different items of the institution?

Report and Evaluation

1. What sort of reports are prepared by your institution?

2. What methods of mass media are used to inform public about the services of your institution?

3. Do you follow any public relations policy?

4. Do you entertain the complaints received from the public? Yes/No.

If yes, what are the types of complaints?

What do you do with the complaints?

Can you take action on the complaints?

If not, what are the causes? (Please specify.)

Do you maintain any progress report?

How do you assess the programme of your agency?

SCHEDULE 'C'

Interview Schedule for Paramedicals, Sanitarians and Extension Educators, Nurses attached to Family Welfare Planning Centres

1. Name of the Institution.

2. Designation.

3. What are your duties?

(a) Do you have any written record of your duties? Yes/No.

(b) Who prescribes your duties?

4. (a) What is the area you are supposed to cover?

   (b) Is it much more than you can properly cover?

5. What is the average number of cases you have to deal with per month?

   (a) Do you think it is more than you can efficiently look into?

   (b) What do you think should be the ideal number of cases?

6. (a) Do you get opportunity to make use of your technical/professional knowledge?

   (b) How do the general public feel about your ability to deal with cases?

   (c) How do your superior officers feel about your ability to handle the cases?

7. What do you feel as member of public about the ability and promptness with which your medical problems are dealt with by the Corporation Health Department?

8. (a) Do you take part in the management of your institution/unit? Yes/No.

   (b) If yes, please give examples.

9. (a) Does the head of your Section/Unit consult you on any matter about the working of the department? Yes/No.

   (b) If yes, give some examples.

10. (a) Does anybody supervise your work?

    (b) Are you satisfied with the type of supervision?

11. (a) During the course of your work do you face problems where you need someone's help? Yes/No.

    (b) If yes, give examples to testify your case.

    (c) Whom do you approach on such matters?

    (d) Are you satisfied on the action taken?

12. Are you encouraged to join seminars, conferences arranged by the professional organisations to further your professional knowledge?

13. (a) Have you ever in your day to day dealings met any situation where you found the health bye-laws are ineffective? Yes/No.

    (b) If yes, please give examples.

14. Do you suggest any change in the health bye-laws for providing effective service to the people?

15. (a) Are you satisfied with your present job? Yes/No.

    (b) Do you have prospect for promotion in this job? Yes/No.

16. (a) Would you like to continue here or leave this place as soon as you get opportunity somewhere else? Yes/No.

    (b) If yes, why?

17. (a) Are you satisfied with your service conditions? Yes/No.

    (b) If no, what are your grievances?

18. (a) What is your overall experience and impression of the working of the family planning programme in your area?

    (b) Give some suggestions as to how it could be improved?

19. Do you feel that the resources/medicine/accommodation/equipments provided to you are adequate for proper implementation of the programme?

20. (a) Are you satisfied with the amount of people's cooperation in the implementation of the programme? Yes/No.

    (b) If yes, where do they cooperate most (please specify)?

    (c) if no, what are the areas where they are most uncooperative?

    (d) What measures do you suggest to enlist maximum cooperation from the people?

21. (a) Do you feel that enough has been done towards public relations? Yes/No.

    (b) if no, what more should be done?

22. (a) What is your relationship with the voluntary agencies on health or family planning services working in your area?

    (b) If it is not cordial, please specify why it is so?

SCHEDULE 'D'

Interview Schedule on personal data to be used as supplementary to Schedules A, B and C

1. Name of the individual
2. Designation
3. Age
4. Education   1. Matric, Non-Matric
                     2. Graduate
                     3. Technical/Professional
                     4. P.H. Training
                     5. Any other.
5. Did you have any other training since you obtained your degree? Yes/No.
6. (a) Have you been abroad? Yes/No.
    (b) If yes, what was the purpose of visit?
         Who sponsored it?
7. Do you belong to any professional, social or other kind of association? (Please give details.)
8. What are your duties?
9. What positions, if any, have you held before joining this position?
10. When did you join the present organisation? In what position?
11. Why did you prefer this present job?
12. What were your expectations when you joined and what are your experiences during your stay here?
    frustration/fulfilment/nothing spectacular
13. How differently would you like the organisation to be run?
14. Is your emolument adequate?
15. Do you desire job satisfaction with your work?
16. Do you feel that you are given proper recognition and appreciation for your job?
17. (a) It is usually said that the heads of the units, Deputy Directors and the hospital Superintendents are too much busy with routine procedure and administrative matters and have very little time for inspection or actual involvement with the provision of services?

(b) Do you think this is true?

(c) What steps do you suggest to avoid this state of affairs?

18. (a) It was said that general administrator being in charge of administration of health services (Deputy Commissioner) and Administrative Officer (Health) there is too much adherence to rules? Do you agree with this statement?

(b) If yes, why do you think so? (please specify)

19. Do you think you might leave this job any moment? If yes, why?

20. Since joining present job have you been offered any opportunities for employment outside this organisation? Yes/No.

If yes, why did you not go?

21. What are the special problems you encounter in dealing with your activity?

22. Are you in a position to take independent decision on a problem case without referring to the superiors?

23. What is your opinion about your relationship with your superior?

24. Some of you went on strike twice during the last two years, what are the grievances? (Please specify.)

25. Have they been looked into since then?

26. Do you make public or the authorities responsible about your hazardous working condition?

Public/authority.

27. (a) Have you made any attempt to inform the public about your difficulties? Yes/No.

(b) If no, what are the causes?

28. Should the beneficiaries be made to pay for health services?

29. It is often said that under the present circumstances family planning programme by itself cannot be successful.

(a) Do you agree with this statement? Yes/No.

(b) If no, why do you think so? (Please specify cause.)

30. (a) Are public quite satisfied with your work? Yes/No.

(b) If no, why?

(c) Have you made any attempt to improve the situation?

Index